OXFORD LIBRARY OF THE PHYSICAL SCIENCES

Editors

THE FUNDAMENTAL
ATOMIC CONSTANTS

BY

J. H. SANDERS

FELLOW AND TUTOR OF
ORIEL COLLEGE, OXFORD

UNIVERSITY   LECTURER
AND DEMONSTRATOR

OXFORD UNIVERSITY PRESS
1961

Oxford University Press, Amen House, London E.C.4

GLASGOW NEW YORK TORONTO MELBOURNE WELLINGTON
BOMBAY CALCUTTA MADRAS KARACHI KUALA LUMPUR
CAPE TOWN IBADAN NAIROBI ACCRA

© *Oxford University Press 1961*

Printed in Northern Ireland at The Universities Press, Belfast

PREFACE

Much has been written, mainly in review articles, on the derivation of the most acceptable values of the atomic constants from the wealth of experimental data which is available. It is hoped that this short monograph will provide a concise account of the situation as it exists at present.

I have deliberately tried to refrain from comment on the relative merits of experiments, except where I believe the criticism to be generally acceptable; it has been difficult in a few cases not to depart from this rule. A major task of the reviewer is the assessment of the meaning of the error or uncertainty which an experimenter attaches to his numerical result. I have avoided the problem by stating in all instances the published errors; the reader must refer to the original sources for the interpretation to be placed upon them. It is equally beyond the scope of this book to attempt any criticism of the methods used in deriving the best values of the constants, from the point of view of either the handling of the experimental data or the analytical procedure.

I owe a profound debt to the authors of the works already published on the subject, notably Dr. E. R. Cohen, Prof. J. W. M. DuMond, Prof. J. A. Bearden and their collaborators, who have followed the pioneer, Prof. R. T. Birge, in providing a set of working values of the constants. My interest in the subject has been greatly stimulated by discussions with Prof. DuMond, Prof. P. A. Franken, Dr. L. Essen, Dr. R. D. Huntoon and many others. I am grateful to the Royal Society, the American Physical Society, Dr. K. D. Froome and Dr. J. A. Hipple for permission to use published diagrams. Prof. B. Bleaney and Mr. J. F. Ward read the entire manuscript, Dr. L. Essen the chapter on the velocity of light, and Dr. G. W. Series the section on the Rydberg constant. I am very much indebted to them for their valuable suggestions, and to my wife for her assistance in the preparation of the manuscript.

J. H. S.

CLARENDON LABORATORY, OXFORD
August 1960

CONTENTS

In spite of the delusive word "Constants" that appears in the title, it is the continual variation in the values of these quantities that furnishes most of the interest in the subject.

RAYMOND T. BIRGE

CHAPTER I

THE CHOICE OF CONSTANTS

FROM the quantitative study of the phenomena of physics has emerged the fact that certain quantities appear in reproducible amounts fixed by nature. Among them may be cited the magnitude of the charge on the electron, the mass of the electron, the velocity of electromagnetic radiation in free space, Planck's constant, and so on. Quantities of this sort, which are not expressible in terms of each other, are called the fundamental constants. Attempts have been made, notably by Eddington [62], to find a unified cosmological theory from which the constants and their magnitudes naturally emerge, but such theories have not found universal acceptance.

The fundamental constants of physics are listed in Table I.

TABLE I

The magnitude of the electronic charge, e.
The mass of the electron, m.
The mass of the proton, M.
The velocity of electromagnetic radiation in free space, c.
Planck's constant, h.
Avogadro's number, N.
Boltzmann's constant, k.
The gravitational constant, G.

Of these the last two may be treated here as exceptions in the list, since neither plays a significant role in atomic phenomena. The gravitational constant has been the subject of much theoretical research by such workers as Weyl [183], Eddington [63], Milne [123], and Dirac [49]; from the experimental viewpoint it is a constant which has to be determined directly since it does not appear in combination with any of the other constants in a measurable form. Boltzmann's constant is of the realms of statistical physics, and while it has relations with the atomic constants in, for example, the theories of thermal radiation and thermionic emission, its determination is based on the measurements of classical, rather than atomic, physics.

The other constants e, m, M, c, h, and N form an important group, known as the atomic constants, which appear in related forms in a wide range of phenomena in atomic physics. To give an example, the Rydberg constant R_∞ of spectroscopy is equal to $2\pi^2me^4/h^3c$ and can be measured with an extremely small uncertainty; it thus fixes this relation between the constants. Recently a number of new relations of this type have been measured with high precision. It is the purpose of this monograph to give a brief survey of the earlier measurements on which our knowledge of the constants was based, then to describe in more detail the measurements which lead to the values which are accepted at present.

CHAPTER II

EARLY MEASUREMENTS

2.1. Direct determination of the constants

ALTHOUGH in principle the direct determination of most of the atomic constants is possible, in some cases it is either impracticable or imprecise. Only in the determination of c is the direct method the most precise; the measurement of this important constant is described in Chapter III. The direct determination of Avogadro's number has an uncertainty a few times greater than that of the indirect value obtained from measurements related to N and the other constants. Apart from these, and the direct measurement of e by the oil-drop method, which is now of historic importance only, there has been no attempt to measure the other atomic constants directly.

2.2. The electronic charge, e

Once the existence of the electron had been established in 1897 attempts were made by Townsend [173], H. A. Wilson [190], and J. J. Thomson [171] to measure its charge. These methods gave only the order of magnitude of e; not until Millikan devised his celebrated oil-drop experiment [121] was any precise determination made. In this method the gravitational force on a charged oil-drop was compared with the force due to a vertical electric field by measuring the terminal velocity of the drop in air under various combinations of gravitational and electrical fields. Millikan's result had subsequently to be corrected [90] because he had used an incorrect value for the viscosity of air. The oil-drop method has subsequently been repeated by Hopper and Laby [89], by Bäcklin and Flemberg [10], and by Ishida, Fukushima, and Suetsugu [97]; these measurements, with those of Millikan, have been surveyed by Birge [25]. Interest in them has, however, subsided as far as the precise value of e is concerned; while the oil-drop experiment as devised by Millikan is a monumental piece of fine technique it has been superseded by the indirect determination of e from modern precise measurements. Millikan's quoted uncertainty of $\pm 0 \cdot 008 \times 10^{-10}$ esu (1700 ppm) in his determination of e may be compared with that of the recently deduced value $e = (4 \cdot 80286 \pm 0 \cdot 00009) \times 10^{-10}$ esu (19 ppm) [43].*

2.3. Avogadro's number, N

The value of Avogadro's number N may be found by a method which is lengthy but nevertheless direct in the sense that it does not involve any of the other constants.

If M is the molecular weight of a substance which, for simplicity, will be assumed to have a cubic crystalline structure, d is the length of one edge of the cubic cell, f is the number of molecules in each cell, and ρ is the density of the crystal, then since N is the number of molecules in one gram mole it is also equal to $Mf/d^3\rho$. Of these quantities ρ is found by conventional techniques, M either by chemical means or by mass spectrographic measurements of isotopic weights and isotope abundances, f is known from the crystalline form, and d is

---

* Relative uncertainties are quoted in parts per million (ppm) as deduced from the stated absolute values, with the $\pm$ sign omitted.

measured by the diffraction of X-rays whose wavelength λ is determined ultimately by use of a ruled grating. If the crystal is not cubic the factor d^3 has to be replaced by a term which depends on the shape of the unit cell and the spacing of the diffraction planes in the crystal.

The difficulty of the production and use of a ruled grating for the measurement of X-ray wavelengths has led to the use of calcite as a standard crystal for wavelength determination. The diffraction angle θ in the Bragg equation $n\lambda = 2d' \sin \theta$ may be determined far more precisely than can the value of d', the effective spacing of the diffraction planes, i.e. the actual spacing multiplied by the refractive index of the crystal for the X-rays used. For this reason Siegbahn [162] defined the effective grating spacing d' of calcite at 18°C for first order diffraction ($n = 1$) as 3029·040 X-units (XU). This value was chosen in the belief that one XU was exactly equal to 10^{-11} cm. Subsequent work has, however, shown that the XU is larger than 10^{-11} cm by approximately 0·2 per cent. The value of the conversion factor Λ, by which wavelengths in XU are multiplied to convert them to centimetres, is found by comparing wavelengths measured by a calcite crystal and a ruled grating using the technique developed by Compton and Doan [45] and Thibaud [169]. Such experiments have been done by Bearden [12], Söderman [163], Bäcklin [9], and Tyrén [177], whose results lead [25] to a value of $\Lambda = (1·002030 \pm 0·000020) \times 10^{-11}$. Once again, however, the value deduced by indirect means from related precise measurements (see Chapter V) is of higher precision.

Molecular weights may be measured either on the chemical or physical scale. The chemical scale takes oxygen as having an atomic weight of exactly 16, but it was defined before isotopes had been discovered. It is now known that oxygen has three stable isotopes O^{16}, O^{17}, and O^{18}, all of which occur in natural oxygen in proportions which vary slightly with the origin of the sample. It is evident that the chemical scale is inexactly defined; the physical scale, on the other hand, takes the mass of the O^{16} isotope as exactly 16 atomic mass units and no uncertainty arises. The two scales obviously differ, the chemical unit being the larger. The conversion factor used by the International Commission on Atomic Weights is 1·000275, with an uncertainty of about ±0·000005. The value of Avogadro's number, therefore, depends on the scale of molecular weights used, that is, which scale is used in determining M in the X-ray method described above. In stating the value of N the scale of molecular weights used must accordingly be specified.

The density of a number of crystalline substances has been found by several workers: calcite by Bearden [13], lithium fluoride by C. A. Hutchison and Johnston [94], sodium chloride by Johnston and D. A. Hutchison [100], and potassium chloride by D. A. Hutchison [95]. The grating spacing of calcite has been found by Bearden [14], of sodium chloride, diamond, and potassium chloride by Tu [176], and of lithium fluoride by Straumanis, Ievens, and Karlsons [168]. Birge [25] has surveyed these results and from them deduced a value for N of $(6·02503 \pm 0·00043) \times 10^{23}$ gm mole^{-1} (71 ppm) on the physical scale of atomic weights. The more modern indirect value [43] is essentially in agreement with this, but has an uncertainty nearly three times smaller.

2.4. The Faraday

The charge on the electron, e, and Avogadro's number, N, may be determined directly; the former, however, can be found only with an uncertainty of about 1600 ppm, while N can be found to better than 70 ppm. The Faraday, F, defined as the quantity of electrical charge associated in electrolysis with one gram-equivalent of the substance or substances taking part in the electrochemical reaction, is evidently equal to the product (Ne/c). When the measured value of F is combined with the value of N, a value for e is obtained which has a much smaller uncertainty than that of the oil-drop method. The electrochemical determination of the Faraday is, however, by no means straightforward, the sources of error being partly inherent in the type of cell and the electrolyte used, and partly due to the uncertainties in atomic weights and the conversion of electrical units. Three types of cell have been used, employing silver [150] [158], iodine [11] [181] and sodium oxalate [47] [187]. Of these, the silver method has the greatest number of sources of error; iodine is thought to give the best value, and while the sodium oxalate method seems to be capable of high precision it has given a result in agreement with the silver rather than the iodine cell.

2.5. The specific charge of the electron, e/m

The mass of the electron has not been measured directly, but a great number of experiments have been done to measure the charge-to-mass ratio of the electron, e/m. The first of these was J. J. Thomson's celebrated experiment [172] which established the existence of the electron. Since then a number of ingenious methods have been devised and carried out, too many to describe in detail here. Some of these, such as the methods used by J. J. Thomson himself, by Kaufman [103], Bucherer [32], Kirchner [105], Dunnington [59], Classen [36], Busch [33], Wolf [192], and Shaw [161] used various combinations of magnetic and electric fields and from their observed effect on an electron beam deduced the value of e/m. In other methods, such as those of Weichert [182], Hammer [86], Kirchner [106], and Perry and Chaffee [134] the flight of electrons of known energy was timed over a known distance. Most of these methods must be suspected of having systematic errors of unknown magnitude due to an effect which was not discovered until the 1930's: this is the formation in the vicinity of an electron beam of insulating films on metal surfaces [137] [161] [166]. These films become charged and disturb the electric potential in their vicinity; the energy of the electron beam cannot then be taken as determined by the potential of the electrodes but may differ from the expected value by several volts. Dunnington varied the energy of his electron beam and by extrapolating to infinite electron velocity tried to eliminate the effect. Shaw's method based on focusing in crossed electric and magnetic fields was deliberately designed to produce a result that was independent of the electron velocity. Recent experiments from which e/m may be indirectly deduced involve a measurement of the so-called cyclotron frequency $(He/2\pi mc)$ of electrons in a magnetic field H. This is independent of the electron velocity in the non-relativistic region, but may be disturbed by the presence of non-uniform electric fields (see Chapter IV).

A further type of experiment which yields a value of e/m is the measurement of the Zeeman splitting of spectral lines. It is of lower precision than the deflection or time-of-flight methods already referred to, but is of interest because it involves not free electrons, but electrons bound in atoms. The energy levels of an atom in a singlet state have a g-factor close to unity, the difference from unity, which is of the order of 10–1000 ppm, being due to diamagnetic and relativistic effects. Each level splits in a magnetic field H into a number of sub-levels separated by an energy nearly equal to $\mu_0 H$, where μ_0 is the Bohr magneton $(he/4\pi mc)$. The wavelength differences $\Delta\lambda$ of the observed "normal" triplet spectral line are measured. In the relation

$$\Delta\lambda = \frac{a\lambda^2 H}{4\pi}\left(\frac{e}{mc}\right), \tag{2.1}$$

λ is the wavelength of the line in zero field and a is a factor close to unity which depends on the g-values and magnetic quantum numbers of the levels; from it the value of e/mc can be deduced. The velocity of light is known to a precision much greater than the value of $\Delta\lambda$, so does not limit the precision of e/m. Babcock [8] was the first to use the method; subsequently Campbell and Houston [34] and Kinsler and Houston [104] made precise measurements in the spectra of zinc, cadmium, helium and neon, which all have suitable singlet levels. Kinsler and Houston quoted a result $(1 \cdot 7570 \pm 0 \cdot 0007) \times 10^8$ emu g^{-1} (400 ppm) which shows no significant difference from the value for the free electron.

2.6. The ratio h/e

Planck's constant h is the fundamental unit of angular momentum which appears throughout atomic and nuclear physics in integral and half-integral multiples. It cannot be measured directly with any precision, though an estimate of its value might be made by observing gyromagnetic phenomena such as the Einstein–de Haas effect. Early attempts to measure it precisely were based largely on determinations of h/e, which can be found

    (a) from photoelectric measurements in the optical range of wavelengths;

    (b) from the photo-ionization of atoms by X-rays;

    (c) from measurements of the excitation and ionization potentials of atoms involving the valence electrons; and

    (d) from measurements of the upper frequency limit of the continuous X-ray spectrum.

These will be referred to separately and briefly.

    (a) The Einstein equation

$$eV = h\nu - e\phi, \tag{2.2}$$

relating the observed kinetic energy eV of an electron liberated from a metal surface of work function ϕ by a photon of frequency ν, may be used to measure h/e. In practice the retarding potential V necessary to stop the photoelectric current is found for a number of values of ν, thus eliminating the need for a knowledge of $e\phi$; typically ν is in or near the visible region and V varies up to a volt or so. As Dubridge [54] and Roehr [147] have pointed out, Einstein's equation assumes that the electrons in the metal have a distribution of energies with a definite upper limit. Because of the Fermi energy distribution of the electrons this state of affairs exists only at absolute zero, and at other temperatures V is not only different from that given by Einstein's equation, but has no sharp value. However, these considerations lead to an uncertainty comparable with the other errors of the experiment. The experimental difficulties include ensuring that the work function ϕ, a notoriously capricious quantity, remains constant throughout the experiment and that scattered light falling on surfaces other than the photo-cathode does not disturb the measurement of the threshold potential V by releasing spurious photo-currents.

Millikan [122] devised an ingenious "lathe in a vacuum" for producing clean and reproducible surfaces of sodium and lithium, and later determinations were made by Lukirsky and Prilezeav [114] and Olpin [131]. As far as their results can be compared, these workers agree only to about 5000 ppm, which illustrates the difficulty of the measurements and makes them the least precise of the group.

(b) An electron may be removed from one of the filled shells of an atom by bombardment either with sufficiently energetic X-rays or with sufficiently energetic electrons. At the threshold the energy eV of the bombarding electrons is just equal to the ionization energy of the atom for the particular electron ejected. This electron will also cause a sharp edge at a certain wavelength λ_e in the X-ray absorption spectrum, due to the onset of photoionization. Equating the electron and photon energies gives the relation

$$\frac{hc}{e} = \lambda_e V \tag{2.3}$$

from which h/e may be found, since c is known with more than adequate precision. In practice λ_e is measured in XU by using a calcite crystal, so the determination involves a knowledge of the conversion factor Λ from XU to cm. The method has been used by Bearden and Schwarz [16], and by Nilsson [129]; the former workers investigated the K electrons of nickel, copper, zinc, and gallium and the L electrons of tungsten, and Nilsson the K electrons of iron, cobalt, nickel, and copper. The method yields a result for h/e to a precision of about 100 ppm.

(c) Many investigations of the excitation and ionization by electron bombardment of atoms in a gas have been made since the pioneer work of Franck and Hertz [72]. The measurement of the minimum energy eV of an electron needed to excite an energy level of an atom from its ground state, combined with a spectroscopic determination of the wavelength λ of the photon resulting from a transition between the same levels, gives

$$\frac{hc}{e} = \lambda V. \tag{2.4}$$

The work of Lawrence [113], Van Atta [178], and Whiddington and Woodroofe [185] on the ionization potentials of mercury, helium, neon, and argon has been used by Dunnington [60] to give a value for h/e which has an uncertainty of about 3000 ppm. Later Dunnington, Hemenway, and Rough [61] made a precise determination of the $^1S_0 \rightarrow ^1P_1$ excitation energy in helium by bombarding the gas with electrons of known energy. The experiment, made with the same type of apparatus as used by Dunnington [59] in his determination of e/m, is open to the same type of criticism concerning the effects of charged surface films and space charge, although care was taken to eliminate or correct for these as far as possible. Using the very much more precisely known wavelength of the appropriate line in the helium spectrum Dunnington quoted a result for h/e with an uncertainty of about 150 ppm.

(d) The upper frequency limit of the continuous X-ray spectrum gives a value of h/e more precise than any of the other methods discussed, and indeed, is a measurement of importance at the present day for evaluating the atomic constants. It has rightly received a great deal of attention, but reference to all the early work in this field is beyond the scope of this book. Reduced to its simplest form, the theory of the method is based on the fact that electrons of energy eV falling on a solid target produce a continuous spectrum of X-rays or Bremsstrahlung from zero frequency to an upper limit which is generated when an electron loses all its kinetic energy in the formation of a single photon. In terms of the lower wavelength limit λ_0 of the spectrum, measured in practice in XU, the relation is

$$\frac{h}{e} = \frac{\Lambda \lambda_0 V}{c} \tag{2.5}$$

where Λ is the wavelength conversion factor from XU to cm. The potential V which determines the energy eV of the electrons inside the target is equal to $(V_0 + \phi)$, the sum of the potential difference V_0 applied between the cathode and the anode of the X-ray tube, and the work function ϕ of the cathode surface. The estimation of the exact limit of the X-ray spectrum is difficult for several reasons: (i) the X-ray spectrometer used has finite resolution and distorts the shape of the observed limit; in Fig. 1 the true shape of the spectrum is assumed to have a sharp limit, and as can be seen, this sharp

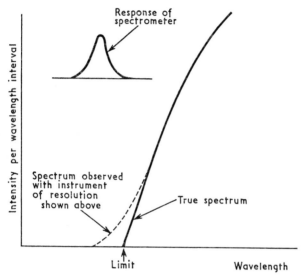

FIG. 1. The lower wavelength limit of the continuous X-ray spectrum.

limit is smoothed out by the poor resolution of the spectrometer; (ii) the experiment has, in order to obtain sufficient intensity, to be performed with a thick target, instead of one which is so thin that the electrons, in passing through it, make not more than one collision with an atom which generates Bremsstrahlung; in the latter case the spectrum would have the form shown in Fig. 2(a), whereas the observed thick target spectrum has the less desirable shape shown in Fig. 2(b). The resolving power of the spectrometers available is not sufficient to show the true shape of the limit. This point has been discussed fully by DuMond [57], who infers that there may be a discontinuity as shown at A in Fig. 2(c). In addition the spectrum shows irregularities of shape near the limit, first discovered by Ohlin [130], which may confuse the deduction of the true limit from the experimental data. The nature of the spectrum near the lower wavelength limit and the cause of the Ohlin irregularities are so far unexplained. Improvements in instrumental resolution and in the understanding of the

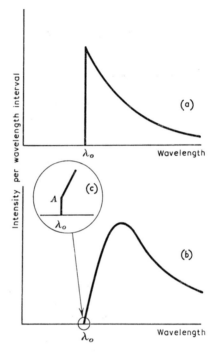

FIG. 2. Continuous X-ray spectra for thin and thick targets.

form of the limit resulted in a steady increase of the deduced value of h/e from $1 \cdot 3749 \times 10^{-17}$ erg sec esu^{-1} in 1921, when it was first measured with an attempt at good precision by Duane, Palmer, and Yeh [53], to $(1 \cdot 37928 \pm 0 \cdot 0004) \times 10^{-17}$ erg sec esu^{-1}, Bearden, Johnson, and Watts' value [15] of 1951. Part of the discrepancy of these figures is due to the change in the accepted values of c and Λ between 1921 and 1951. A full account of the experimental results has been given by Cohen, Crowe, and DuMond [40].

2.7. The Rydberg constant

In an article published in 1890 Rydberg [152] proposed that the wavelengths λ of the lines in the series which were found in the spectra of the alkali metals were related by the expression

$$\frac{1}{\lambda} = \frac{1}{\lambda_0} - \frac{N_0}{(n+\mu)^2}, \tag{2.6}$$

where λ_0 is the wavelength of the limit of the series, n is an integer, μ is a small quantity (later called the quantum defect) dependent on the series and the atom under consideration, and N_0 is a universal constant. He found the value of N_0 to be 109721·6 cm^{-1} when the wavelengths were measured in standard air. Later, Bohr showed that the wavelengths of the lines in the spectrum of single electron atoms with a nuclear charge $+Ze$ are given by

$$\frac{1}{\lambda} = RZ^2 \left(\frac{1}{n_1^2} - \frac{1}{n_2^2} \right), \tag{2.7}$$

where n_1 and n_2 are integers and R is a constant known, when the wavelengths are measured in vacuum, as the Rydberg constant. The value of the Rydberg constant is given by

$$R = R_\infty \left(1 + \frac{m}{M_0} \right), \tag{2.8}$$

where m is the mass of the electron and M_0 is the mass of the nucleus of the atom; R_∞ is known as the Rydberg constant for infinite mass and has the value $2\pi^2 m e^4/h^3 c$.

The evaluation of R_∞ from spectroscopic data is complicated by the presence of the fine structure of the spectral lines which is not taken into account in the Bohr theory. Adequate theoretical expressions for the wavelengths of the fine structure components in terms of R_∞ exist only for single electron atoms. Houston [91] has measured the wavelengths of lines in the spectra of hydrogen and ionized helium, Chu [35] in ionized helium, and Drinkwater, Richardson, and Williams [51] in hydrogen and deuterium. All these determinations were made when the Dirac theory was believed to be adequate for the description of the fine structure of these atoms; later, deviations from this theory, known as the 'Lamb shift' were explained by quantum electrodynamics [159]. The experimental data were reviewed by Cohen [38] in the light of this new theory and the necessary small correction to the deduced value of the Rydberg constant was made. Both Houston's and Chu's measurements give a value for R_∞ which is not in agreement with that of Drinkwater, Richardson, and Williams. Houston and Chu had used as a standard the value of $5015 \cdot 6750$ Å for the wavelength in standard air of the $2^1S_0-3^1P_1$ line in the spectrum of helium. This value had been obtained earlier by Merrill [118] in terms of the wavelength of the red line of cadmium which defines the International Ångström scale. Drinkwater, Richardson, and Williams used the cadmium red line itself as a standard and pointed out that the discrepancy probably lay in Houston's use of the He standard. Cohen's analysis was in agreement with this view, and it has since been confirmed experimentally by Field and Series [67] who obtained a value of $5015 \cdot 6775 \pm 0 \cdot 0007$ Å for the line, the use of which brings Houston's and Chu's results into agreement with the other workers'.

The Rydberg constant, which now has the accepted value of $R_\infty = 109737 \cdot 309 \pm 0 \cdot 012$ cm^{-1} ($0 \cdot 11$ ppm) [43], is among the most precisely known experimental quantities, and is a valuable relation between the fundamental constants which individually are known with far less precision.

2.8. Other measurements related to the atomic constants

Several other measurable quantities are related more or less directly to the atomic constants. A few of these can be measured with exceptionally high precision and will be discussed in Chapters III and IV. Among others which are of interest the following may be mentioned:

(i) *The Rydberg constant for finite nuclear mass*

The Rydberg constant for various atoms is related to the Rydberg constant for infinite nuclear mass by equation (2.8). It is evident that measurements of R for different values of M_0 will yield, without a knowledge of R_∞, a value for m, in gm, provided M_0 is known in gm. Since the value of M_0 depends on a knowledge of the value of Avogadro's number N it is more usual to express M_0 in atomic mass units, when 2.8 becomes

$$R = R_\infty\left(1 + \frac{Nm}{M_0}\right) \qquad (2.9)$$

where m is in gm, M_0 is in amu, and N is measured on the physical scale. The quantity Nm is sometimes referred to as "the atomic mass of the electron". Measurements of the H_α and D_α lines by Shane and Spedding [160], Robinson [145], and Williams [189], with mass spectrographic values for the masses of the proton and the deuteron, have been used by Cohen [38] to find a value for Nm with an uncertainty of 150 ppm. These measurements were also used by him to confirm the suspected error in the wavelength standard used by Houston and Chu mentioned in section 2.7.

(ii) *The Compton wavelength shift*

When a photon is scattered through an angle θ by a free electron it suffers a change of wavelength

$$\Delta\lambda = (h/mc)(1 - \cos\theta).$$

This simple expression, corrected to allow for the fact that the electrons were bound to atoms and not free, has been used by Ross and Kirkpatrick [151] to determine (h/mc) to about 1500 ppm.

(iii) *The de Broglie wavelength of electrons*

An electron of momentum p has a wavelength $\lambda = h/p$ which may be found by diffracting the electrons by a crystal lattice of known spacing. Rymer and Wright [153] produced electrons of known momentum by accelerating them through a potential difference V close to $50\,\mathrm{kV}$ and then diffracted them with various crystals. The relativistic relation between momentum and kinetic energy gives the relation

$$\frac{h}{(em)^{\frac{1}{2}}} = \lambda\left(\frac{2V}{c}\right)^{\frac{1}{2}}\left(1 + \frac{eV}{2mc^2}\right)^{\frac{1}{2}}. \qquad (2.10)$$

The value of the second bracket was about 1·025, so that e/m did not have to be known with high precision. The wavelength

λ was converted from XU to cm by use of the factor Λ. The value of $h/(em)^{\frac{1}{2}}$ was found to about 70 ppm; with slight refinement the method is likely to be of considerable value in determining the values of the constants.

(iv) *The wavelength of positron annihilation radiation*

The usual fate of positrons brought to rest in matter is to combine with a stationary electron to give two photons of equal energy travelling in opposite directions. The wavelength of each photon is equal to h/mc; the energy of the photon is the rest-energy of an electron, i.e. about 0·51 MeV, corresponding to a wavelength of roughly 25 XU. DuMond and his collaborators [58] [126] have measured the wavelength using a crystal spectrometer (which requires the use of the XU conversion factor Λ) and have shown that the velocity of the positron is effectively zero when it is annihilated, as assumed in deriving the expression for the wavelength of the radiation. Their result is quoted to about 100 ppm and it is believed [40] that the method could be improved to compete in precision with the X-ray lower wavelength limit determination of h/e.

(v) *X-ray photoelectron energies*

When an atom is photo-ionized the ejected electron has kinetic energy E equal to the photon energy hc/λ less the ionization energy E_i of the atom. This ionization energy is related to the wavelength λ_i of the corresponding absorption edge for the element by the relation $E_i = (hc/\lambda_i)$, with a small correction for the valence binding of the atom. If the radius of curvature r of the electrons is measured in a magnetic field H the result may be used to derive the ratio e^2/hm from the relation

$$\frac{e^2}{hm} = \frac{2c^3}{H^2 r^2}\left(\frac{1}{\lambda} - \frac{1}{\lambda_i}\right)\left(1 + \frac{E}{2mc^2}\right) \tag{2.11}$$

where the last factor differs from unity by a small relativistic correction which requires an approximate knowledge of the value of h/mc. The method has been used by Kretschmar [109] and by Robinson and his collaborators [37] [146]; the latter quote a final result with an uncertainty of 500 ppm.

(vi) *The radiation constants*

Though the practical interest of the relations between the quantities appearing in the laws of radiation and the atomic constants is insignificant, they deserve mention because of their fundamental nature. Planck's distribution law for black body radiation can be stated as

$$I_\lambda \, d\lambda = \frac{C_1 d\lambda}{\lambda^5 (e^{C_2/\lambda T} - 1)} \qquad (2.12)$$

where $I_\lambda \, d\lambda$ is the power radiated in the wavelength range λ to $\lambda + d\lambda$ from unit area of a black body at an absolute temperature T,

$$C_1 = 2\pi c^2 h \qquad (2.13)$$
$$C_2 = ch/k \qquad (2.14)$$

and k is Boltzmann's constant.

From Planck's law may be derived Stefan's law and the Wien displacement law. The former states that the total power radiated from unit area of a black body is

$$I = \left(\frac{\pi^4}{15}\right)\frac{C_1}{C_2^4} \cdot T^4 = \sigma T^4 \qquad (2.15)$$

where $\sigma = (2\pi^5/15)(k^4/h^3 c^2)$

The Wien displacement law is given by

$$\lambda_m T = C_2/4{\cdot}965 \qquad (2.16)$$

where λ_m is the wavelength at which $I_\lambda \, d\lambda$ is a maximum and the numerical factor arises from finding the root of a transcendental equation. The three practicable types of experiment for finding the values of σ and C_2 are:

(1) measuring the value of Stefan's constant σ by finding the value of I from a black body of known temperature;

(2) measuring the relative values of $I_\lambda \, d\lambda$ at two or more different wavelengths in order to deduce C_2 from (2.12);

(3) measuring the value of $\lambda_m T$ and hence obtaining C_2 from (2.16).

The low precision obtainable by these methods is shown by the summarized results in the review by Bearden and Thomsen [17]:

$$\sigma = (5{\cdot}74 \pm 0{\cdot}03) \times 10^{-5} \text{ erg cm}^{-2} \text{ sec}^{-1} \text{ deg C}^{-4} \quad (5200 \text{ ppm})$$
$$C_2 = (1{\cdot}434 \pm 0{\cdot}002) \text{ cm degC.} \qquad (1400 \text{ ppm})$$

2.9. The derivation of the 'best values' of the constants

From the preceding survey of various measurements of quantities related to the atomic constants it will be evident that it is possible to derive various values of h, e, m, and N by taking suitable different combinations of experimental results. This procedure, used without restraint, would obviously lead to confusion; if different workers used different values of the constants a comparison of their results would be made difficult. In 1929 Birge [27] published the first of a series of reviews in which he discussed the derivation of values of the constants which appeared, from a critical evaluation of the precision of the experiments and an analytical test of the consistency of the results, to be closest to the true values.

Birge started by fixing the values of certain quantities which had been measured so precisely that their values could be taken as independent of any of those which were less well known. Among these "auxiliary" or "exact" constants were the velocity of light, the Rydberg constant and the Faraday. By a succession of steps he then proceeded to evaluate the fundamental constants in what appeared to be the most reasonable way in the light of the available experimental results. Besides establishing and publishing values of the constants accepted and used by the majority of physicists, Birge's surveys were invaluable in revealing and resolving discrepancies in the experimental results, leading to the rejection of those which, through some undiscovered systematic error, did not conform with the rest. Birge's tables of values of the constants were widely published and almost universally used.

With the passage of World War II the situation regarding the fundamental constants changed. A number of new techniques, notably in the electronic and microwave fields, became available and these, with the general increase in scientific effort, resulted in new measurements which rendered obsolete many of those which have been mentioned in this chapter. With the exception of the velocity of light none of the constants has been determined directly by these new techniques, and indeed, many of the measurements are of quantities whose relation to the fundamental constants has a tortuous, rather than simple form. Nevertheless by the use of rather lengthy analytical procedures it is possible to derive "best" values of the constants which have in most cases an appreciably smaller uncertainty than hitherto. The rest of this monograph will be concerned mainly with a description of these recent measurements and the derivation from them of the values of the fundamental constants.

CHAPTER III

THE VELOCITY OF LIGHT

INTEREST in the velocity of electromagnetic radiation in free space, c, originated long before the fundamental nature of the constant was realized. The theory of relativity shows that the significance of c is not confined solely to the propagation of electromagnetic waves. This constant is, for example, the upper limit of the velocity of matter or any other form of energy relative to an observer; it is also the limiting velocity of communication by any process between two observers. Its fundamental relation to physical phenomena is further shown by the fact that it appears in the relations between electric and magnetic units, and in the relation between the units of energy and mass. The connotation 'the velocity of light' by which the quantity c is still generally known is imprecise and restricted, but for convenience this term will be used here.

The velocity of light is the only constant which may be measured directly with higher precision than by indirect means. Present day measurements at optical frequencies (about 5×10^{14} c sec^{-1}) and at microwave frequencies (10^{10} to 10^{11} c sec^{-1}, i.e. 10–100 kMc sec^{-1}) have an uncertainty of about 1 ppm. The good agreement between the results in these two frequency ranges shows that, within the experimental uncertainties there is no reason to doubt that, as predicted by Maxwell's theory, c is independent of the frequency of the radiation. Neither has the suggestion made by Gheury de Bray [81] that the velocity of light is decreasing with time any foundation in view of recent measurements.

3.1. Early measurements

'M. Roëmer commença à former cette conjecture ingénieuse: Que la lumiere pouvoit employer quelque tems à se repandre.'* This comment on the first demonstration that light travels with a finite velocity was made in a report [3] on the progress of science in the year 1676. Earlier attempts by Galileo [78] to demonstrate the finite velocity of light by the well-known lantern method had failed. Römer [148] noticed a systematic variation in the apparent period of revolution of Jupiter's first satellite round its parent planet (the Doppler shift of the period as the earth and Jupiter approached and receded from each other) and correctly explained it by the finite time taken for light to travel through space. From the available observations he deduced '. . . que la lumiere dans une seconde de tems fait 48203 lieuës communes de France et 377/1141 parties d'une de ces lieuës, fraction qui doit bien être négligée.' This result is equivalent to 214200 km sec^{-1}; its error is due mainly to the lack of knowledge of the value of the radius of the earth's orbit. One cannot fail to have respect for the sagacious but inadequate regard shown for the uncertainty of the measurement.

Römer's conjecture was confirmed in 1727 by Bradley [30] who observed the apparent change in the position of the fixed stars due to the motion of the earth in its orbit, the so-called aberration of light. It was not, however, until 1849 that a purely terrestial measurement of c was made, by Fizeau [68] using his celebrated toothed wheel method. This technique was improved and used by Cornu [46] in 1874, by Young and Forbes [193] in 1881 and by Perrotin [133] in 1900 and 1902.

* This, and the later passage, have been copied without alteration from the original; deviations from modern spelling will be noticed.

The difficulty of judging the angular velocity of the toothed wheel at which the returning light is eclipsed renders the method incapable of high precision, and it was superseded by the rotating mirror method in which the displacement of a spot of light is measured. The displacement arises from the angular motion of a rotating mirror during the time the light travels a known large distance, the light being reflected from the mirror before and after travelling over this path. The method was suggested by Wheatstone [184], developed by Arago [4] and Foucault [70] and used by Foucault in 1862 [71]. Later measurements using the method were made by Newcomb [128] in 1885 and by Michelson [119] between 1879 and 1927. Michelson also collaborated with Pease and Pearson [120] in the early stages of the impressive mile-long evacuated pipe experiment which also used the rotating mirror method. The results were published in 1935, after Michelson's death. This experiment failed, because of a systematic error, to give results of the precision for which its designers hoped, or with which its subsequent critics credited it. The source of the error is not fully understood, but may have been due to instability of the baseline or refraction in the unevacuated parts of the light path [19].

The need for modulation of the light beam at frequencies higher than those obtainable by mechanical means brought about the development of electrical shutters. So far two types have been developed, one using the Kerr cell and the other using ultrasonic waves in a quartz crystal. The latter device generates, by the periodic spatial variation of refractive index when ultrasonic waves are propagated in the crystal, a form of optical diffraction grating. This is formed and disappears at twice the ultrasonic frequency and so can be used to produce a diffracted beam which is amplitude modulated. The acoustic waves are generated by placing a piezoelectric crystal in an alternating electric field. This type of light modulator was used in 1937–38 by McKinley [116] at 8 Mc sec^{-1} and in 1949 by Houstoun [92] at 200 Mc sec^{-1}. The results for the velocity of light quoted by these workers are (299780 ± 70) km sec^{-1}

(200 ppm) and (299775 ± 9) km sec^{-1} (30 ppm) respectively. The error limits given in the latter are generally considered to be too narrow. The method has not yet been used for a precise measurement of c.

The Kerr cell uses the property of certain molecular substances of becoming optically active in an electric field; a Kerr cell placed between two crossed polarizers such as Nicol prisms may be used to modulate a light beam at a high frequency if an alternating potential is applied across the cell. The upper frequency limit, determined by the relaxation time of the molecules, is between 10^7 and 10^8 c sec^{-1}. The Kerr cell was first used by Gutton [84] in 1912 to compare the velocity of light in air with the velocity of electromagnetic waves on a transmission line. The velocity of light itself was measured using a Kerr cell by Karolus and Mittelstaedt [101] [124] in 1928–9; a modulation frequency of between 3 and 7 Mc sec^{-1} and a total optical path of about 300 m were used. These figures may be compared with the path of over 70 km and modulation frequencies up to 8 kc sec^{-1} used by Michelson in his 1927 rotating mirror determination. Further measurements using the Kerr cell were made by Anderson [2] in 1937 and 1941 and by Hüttel [96] in 1940. The former used 19 Mc sec^{-1} modulation and a path of 172 m, the latter used frequencies between 5 and 12 Mc sec^{-1} and a path of 80 m.

It was unfortunate that the systematic errors present in four determinations published between 1935 and 1941 should all have given results which were consistently about 20 km

TABLE 2

Workers	Year	Value of c
Michelson, Pease, and Pearson	1935	(299774 ± 4) km sec^{-1} (13 ppm)
Anderson	1937	(299771 ± 10) km sec^{-1} (33 ppm)
Hüttel	1940	(299771 ± 10) km sec^{-1} (33 ppm)
Anderson	1941	(299776 ± 6) km sec^{-1} (20 ppm)

sec^{-1} too low compared with the value accepted now. Birge, in his 1941 review [26] revised the experimenters' results and errors and quoted the four shown in Table 2.

These values, with other earlier determinations, led Birge

to quote a value of (299776 ± 4) km sec^{-1} (13 ppm) for c; the value accepted now is close to 299793 km sec^{-1} with an uncertainty well under ± 1 km sec^{-1} (3 ppm). The possible sources of systematic errors in the experiments have been investigated by Bergstrand [19] [20] who concludes that the results are not necessarily inconsistent with modern determinations. Although Birge's value and its error were generally accepted and used between 1941 and 1949, other reviewers quoted similar values with more conservative limits: Stille [167] in 1943 suggested (299777 ± 20) km sec^{-1} and Dorsey [50], in 1945, (299773 ± 10) km sec^{-1}.

3.2. Post-1941 work

Evidence that Birge's 1941 value for c was erroneous accumulated during the Second World War, when navigational aids based on radar techniques were developed. Distances measured by conventional surveying techniques and by timing a short pulse of radio waves over the same path failed to give the same result when, in the latter case, Birge's value of c was used in computing the distance. Aslakson [5] [7] using the American Shoran method and Hart [88] using the British Oboe blind bombing aid obtained results which led them to question the Birge value of c. Aslakson [6] commented in 1949 'At that time [1947] it was felt that to question the generally accepted determination by Anderson and others of 299776 km/sec would be presumptuous. However in view of recent corroborative evidence ... it is now considered advisable to publish the value of 299792 km/sec as determined by me'. The results quoted in Table 2 have now been abandoned, but they leave behind them a lesson in the significance of undetected systematic errors worthy of the attention of all workers in the field of precise measurements.

The first post-war determination of c, by Essen and Gordon-Smith [65] was made by measuring the wavelength of microwave radiation of known frequency. Many earlier attempts had been made to find the value of c by using this principle, at lower frequencies. Notable among these is the work of

Mercier [117] in 1924, who measured the wavelength of 47 Mc sec^{-1} waves on Lecher wires and obtained a result of $c =$ (299782$\pm$30) km sec^{-1}.

In Essen's and Gordon-Smith's experiment the wavelength was not measured in free space, but in an evacuated cavity resonator. In such a case the free-space wavelength λ is related to the wavelength in the cavity λ_g by the relation

$$\frac{1}{\lambda^2} = \frac{1}{\lambda_g^2} + \frac{1}{\lambda_c^2} \qquad (3.1)$$

where λ_c is a parameter, the critical wavelength, which depends principally on the dimensions of the cavity in a manner related to the mode in which the cavity is excited. Equation (3.1) assumes the cavity walls to be perfectly conducting. When the length of the cavity is altered, the cavity resonates at lengths which differ by $\lambda_g/2$, so that by finding successive resonant lengths and knowing the dimensions of the cavity, and hence λ_c, it is possible to deduce the value of λ. The frequency ν of the microwave radiation used can readily be found in terms of a quartz crystal standard to a precision much higher than that of the other measurements in the experiment, so that c may be found from the relation $c = \nu\lambda$. Using a single cavity of fixed dimensions at a frequency of 3 kMc sec^{-1} (λ about 10 cm) Essen and Gordon-Smith found $c =$ (299792$\pm$9) km sec^{-1} (30 ppm). A small but significant correction is needed to the relation 3.1 above, owing to the fact that the walls of the cavity are not perfectly conducting; however, the correction term is frequency dependent, and may be eliminated by taking a number of measurements at different frequencies. Essen later obtained a more precise value for c by using frequencies between 5 kMc sec^{-1} and 11 kMc sec^{-1} (λ from approximately 6 cm to 2·7 cm) and in 1950 [64] quoted a result of (299792·5$\pm$3) km sec^{-1} (10 ppm).

Similar work initiated by Hansen and completed by Bol [28] in 1950 gave a value of (299789·3$\pm$0·4) km sec^{-1} (1·3 ppm), but is now supposed to have a systematic error due to the presence of the finite conductivity of the walls which was not eliminated experimentally as in Essen's measurements. The theoretical correction which Bol applied was probably inadequate.

At about the same time these values were confirmed by the results of Bergstrand [21] using visible light waves modulated by a Kerr cell, and by the Shoran (300 Mc sec^{-1}) method of Aslakson mentioned above; these workers found c to be (299796 ± 2) km sec^{-1} (7 ppm) and $(299792 \cdot 4 \pm 2 \cdot 4)$ km sec^{-1} (8 ppm) respectively. Later the uncertainties of both these results were reduced, and Aslakson quoted in 1951 [7] a value of $(299794 \cdot 2 \pm 1 \cdot 4)$ km sec^{-1} (5 ppm). At about the same time, Froome [74] developed a form of Michelson's interferometer to measure the wavelength of microwaves (of about 1·25 cm wavelength and precisely known frequency) in air. It gave a result $c = (299792 \cdot 6 \pm 0 \cdot 7)$ km sec^{-1} (2 ppm). A rather similar type of measurement using a much lower frequency, 172·8 Mc sec^{-1}, was made by Florman [69] who quoted $c = (299795 \cdot 1 \pm 3 \cdot 1)$ km sec^{-1} (10 ppm).

The value now accepted for c rests mainly on two types of measurement: one, using microwaves, by Froome at the National Physical Laboratory; the second, using visible light, by Bergstrand and others over various baselines in Sweden, Great Britain, and Australia.

3.3. The microwave interferometer method of Froome

In Froome's experiments [75] [76] the wavelength of microwave radiation was measured under geometrical conditions approximating as closely as possible to those of free space. The experiments were in air, since a vacuum tank of adequate dimensions was quite impracticable. The correction to vacuum was found at the time of the experiments by measuring the difference between the resonant frequencies of a cavity when it contained a sample of the room air and when it was evacuated, the measurement being made with the same frequency as was used in the determination of c.

The main complication of an experiment of this sort is introduced by the difficulty of propagating waves which are

3

either truly plane or truly spherical. Consequently the distances between successive minima or maxima recorded by the interferometer used for measuring the wavelength are not exactly equal to one wavelength or one half wavelength as they would be in the case of plane waves, nor is the relation between them easily calculable as in the case of spherical waves. In practice the waves are radiated from, and received by, horns at the end of waveguides under conditions where diffraction at the horns introduces an appreciable departure from either of the special cases cited. The diffraction correction can, however, successfully be calculated, as shown by the good agreement between Froome's two results derived from experiments in which the magnitude of the corrections was quite different.

Froome performed separate experiments with two interferometers which were identical in principle, one operating at a frequency of 24 kMc sec^{-1} ($\lambda \approx 1{\cdot}25$ cm) and the other at 72 kMc sec^{-1} ($\lambda \approx 4$ mm). A diagram of the latter interferometer is shown in Fig. 3. Microwave power from a klystron (or its second harmonic, generated by a silicon crystal, in the case of the 72 kMc sec^{-1} experiment) was sent through waveguides to the two transmitting horns which face each other. The radiated power arrived at the two receiving horns, fixed together on a movable carriage, each facing a transmitting horn; in order to prevent signals from one transmitting horn entering the wrong receiving horn and affecting the results, the two transmitted waves were polarized at 90° to each other. The signals received at the two horns were added together and the amplitude of the resulting signal after detection was indicated on a meter. As the carriage was moved along the line joining the two transmitting horns, the meter showed maxima and minima, the interval between successive minima being a movement of approximately one half wavelength. A precise value of the wavelength could then be found from the known diffraction correction. The purpose of the constant phase interferometer (c.p.i.) shown in one arm of the transmitter was to alter the amplitude of the signal passing down this arm

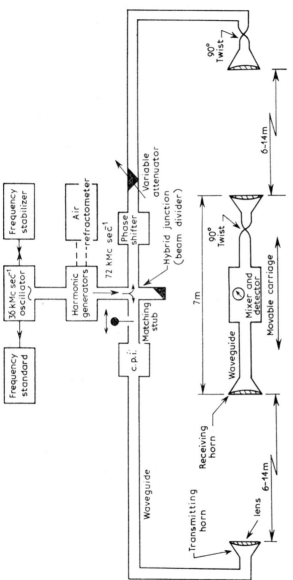

Fig. 3. Diagram of Froome's 72 kMc sec⁻¹ interferometer.

without changing its phase. In this way the two received signals, whose relative amplitude varied considerably as the carriage was moved, could be made equal. The minima could therefore be made sharp at any position of the carriage without introducing an error due to the change of the relative phase of the signals at the transmitting horns.

The carriage was moved through a distance corresponding to 81 wavelengths in the 24 kMc sec^{-1} experiment so that a one-metre length standard could be used; in the 72 kMc sec^{-1} experiment 485 wavelengths and a 2 metre standard were used. In order to eliminate the diffraction error measurements were taken at a number of different initial separations between the transmitting and receiving horns. The magnitude of this correction after the measurements in air had been corrected to a vacuum ranged between approximately 10 and 100 km sec^{-1} in the 24 kMc sec^{-1} case, the magnitude depending on the initial separation. In the 72 kMc sec^{-1} experiment the correction was far smaller, only 0·6 to 3·5 km sec^{-1}. The final results obtained were

24 kMc sec^{-1} experiments: 299792·75±0·3 km sec^{-1}* (1 ppm)

72 kMc sec^{-1} experiments: 299792·5 ±0·1 km sec^{-1} (0·3 ppm)

The main criticism of these measurements is the comparatively large diffraction correction that has to be used, but confidence in the theoretical estimates of the correction is justified by the close agreement of the results obtained in the two determinations, in which the scale of the apparatus was quite different. While it may be argued that a repetition in the same laboratory of an experiment with apparatus which is identical in principle may be subject to some undiscovered systematic error, the good agreement with optical determinations with the geodimeter leads one to suppose that the quoted uncertainty in the results is not unduly optimistic.

---

* The value originally published 299793·0±0·3 km sec^{-1} (1 ppm) [75] was later corrected [77] because of the discovery of an error in the value of the 1 m length standard.

3.4. Bergstrand's method

Bergstrand has refined the use of the Kerr cell to give a very precise measurement of the group velocity of visible light in air v_a over geodetically measured baselines. From this measurement and a knowledge of the atmospheric conditions over the path of the light, the value of c can be found.

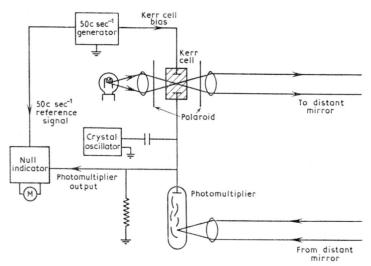

FIG. 4. Diagram of Bergstrand's apparatus (the geodimeter).

The Kerr cell is used between two pieces of Polaroid (Fig. 4). The relation between the light intensity transmitted by such a system and the voltage applied to the electrodes of the Kerr cell is shown in Fig. 5. If the cell is biassed by a steady positive voltage $+V$ on which a high frequency alternating voltage, of amplitude smaller than V, and frequency ν, is superimposed as shown, the light output from the cell will vary according to curve AA. The intensity of the light beam is modulated in this way and its amplitude may be described to a good approximation by the expression

$$I = I_0\{1 + a \sin 2\pi\nu[t - (x/v_a)]\} \qquad (3.2)$$

where a is less than, but close to, unity and x is the distance from the point of observation to the Kerr cell; the phase of the

modulation envelope at the Kerr cell is arbitrarily taken as
zero. The quantity $\phi = 2\pi v x / v_a$ (3.3)
represents the relative phase of the modulation envelope at
the Kerr cell and at the point of observation. Bergstrand's
method provides a particularly precise method of measuring
this relative phase (or rather, of detecting when it is an integral
multiple of π) and consequently v_a may be measured precisely.

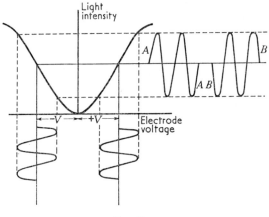

FIG. 5.

The modulated light beam is reflected from a mirror at a
distance D and returns to a photomultiplier cell placed along-
side the Kerr cell. The anode voltage of the photomultiplier
is fed from the same high frequency alternating supply as the
Kerr cell. When the anode is positive, the photomultiplier has
nearly constant sensitivity, but when the anode is negative, it
is completely insensitive, as shown in Fig. 6(a). The mean
photomultiplier current is greatest when the maximum light
intensity coincides with the centre of one of the sensitive half
cycles of the photomultiplier (Figs. 6(a), 6(b), and 6(c)) and the
mean current is least when the maximum light intensity
coincides with the centre of the insensitive half cycle of the
photomultiplier (Figs. 6(a), 6(d), and 6(e)). If the phase ϕ of
the received light is varied, the mean photomultiplier current
passes through maxima and minima as shown in Fig. 7. So far

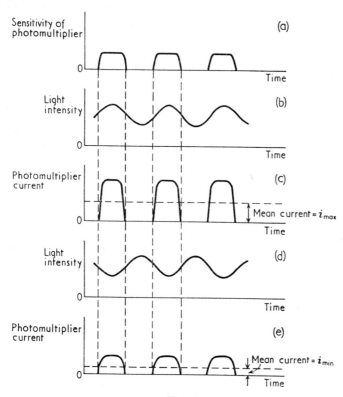

Fig. 6.

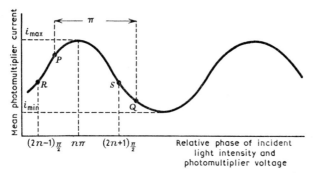

Fig. 7.

the method is identical with that of Hüttel [96], but it is comparatively insensitive as a method of measuring ϕ because of the slow variation of photomultiplier current with phase.

It is possible to change by π the phase relative to the Kerr cell voltage of the light leaving the Kerr cell, and therefore, by the same amount, the phase of the light falling on the photomultiplier relative to the Kerr cell voltage. This is achieved by changing the sign of the bias voltage shown in Fig. 5, which makes the light intensity modulation change in phase relative to the Kerr cell voltage by π (curves AA and BB). The effect of this π phase change is to change the mean photomultiplier current from, say, the value corresponding to point P in Fig. 7 to the value corresponding to point Q. In general these two values of photomultiplier current are different. However, if the effect of changing the phase by π is to go from point R to point S, there will be no change of current. At the points R and S the value of ϕ is $(2n \pm 1)\dfrac{\pi}{2}$, where n is an integer.

Bergstrand changed the polarity of the Kerr cell voltage at 50 c sec^{-1} and used a sensitive electronic circuit to detect equality of the photomultiplier currents during the periods of positive and negative bias. The absolute measurement of the phase ϕ depends on time delays such as that between the arrival of the light waves at the photomultiplier cathode and the resultant signal appearing at the balance detector; for measuring v_a these delays, provided they are constant, are eliminated by finding two values D_1 and D_2 of the mirror distance D at which ϕ is equal to $n_1\pi/2$ and $n_2\pi/2$ respectively, where n_1 and n_2 are both integral. Then from (3.3)

$$(n_1 - n_2)\pi = 8\pi v(D_1 - D_2)/v_a. \tag{3.4}$$

In this equation $(D_1 - D_2)$ is a precisely surveyed distance, v is known by comparison with a standard frequency transmission and $(n_1 - n_2)$ is known unambiguously from an approximate knowledge of the value of v_a.

In his early measurements [21] Bergstrand used a geodetic survey baseline 7 km long, and placed mirrors facing the light source, near its ends. The modulation frequency ν was 8·33 Mc sec^{-1} and the sensitivity of the balance detector was sufficient to indicate a change of D of 4 mm due to a radial displacement of one of the mirrors. The value of c was found from the measured group velocity in air v_a by using the appropriate refractive index deduced from measurements of the pressure, temperature and humidity of the air along the path. Air is dispersive, and, to minimise the uncertainty of the value of the refractive index, a filter passing a narrow colour range was used over the light source. The correction from air to vacuum was about 90 km sec^{-1} with an uncertainty of about 0·18 km sec^{-1}. The result of Bergstrand's preliminary measurements [21] was (299793 ± 2) km sec^{-1} (6 ppm) which he later [22] improved to $(299793 \cdot 1 \pm 0 \cdot 3)$ km sec^{-1} (1 ppm). In the latter measurements the modulation frequency was varied slightly in order to balance the detector with a fixed mirror position.

Bergstrand's apparatus, in slightly modified form, is manufactured under the name "geodimeter" for determining geodetic lengths up to 40 km with an error of 2 parts in 10^6, the velocity of light being assumed. This instrument uses two different modulation frequencies close to 10 Mc sec^{-1} so that the value of $(n_1 - n_2)$ in (3.4) may be found. In this form it has been used to measure c by Mackenzie [115] in Scotland and England $((299792 \cdot 3 \pm 0 \cdot 5)$ km sec^{-1} (1·7 ppm)), by Schöldström [156] in Sweden $((299792 \cdot 4 \pm 0 \cdot 4)$ km sec^{-1} (1·3 ppm)), by Waller [180] in Australia $(299792 \cdot 5$ km sec^{-1}) and by Mears in the United States (unpublished results, see [23]).

3.5. Indirect determinations of c

The constant c appears in Maxwell's electromagnetic theory in the relations between the electrostatic and electromagnetic systems of units. As such it has been measured by several workers, but with particular success in 1907 by Rosa and Dorsey [149], who found the ratio of the capacity of a condenser, calculated in esu from its dimensions, to the value in emu measured from the charge it acquired when a known potential difference was applied. Their value, corrected for the error in the electrical standards they used [26], is (299784 ± 15) km sec^{-1} (50 ppm).

A second indirect method involves the measurement of transitions between the energy levels of a diatomic or linear polyatomic molecule. In the infra-red region the frequencies of the lines in the vibration-rotation spectrum are given to a sufficiently good approximation by the polynomial in m:

$$\nu = \nu_0 + (B_0 + B_1)m + (B_0 - B_1 - D_0 + D_1)m^2$$
$$-2(D_0 + D_1)m^3 - (D_0 - D_1)m^4$$

where ν_0 is the frequency of the band centre, B_0, D_0, and B_1, D_1 are pairs of constants appropriate to the lower and upper rotational states respectively, and $m = J + 1$ ($J = 0, 1, 2, \ldots$) for the R branch and $m = -J$ ($J = 1, 2, 3, \ldots$) for the P branch. In the microwave region transitions between the rotational levels in the ground (vibrational) state are given by

$$\nu = 2B_0(J + 1) - 4D_0(J + 1)^3$$

The constants B_0 and D_0 may be deduced both from infra-red and from microwave measurements, but in the former case their values are found in terms of *wavelength* measurements, and in the latter case in terms of *frequencies*. The ratio of the values found in the two ways gives a value for c. The constant B_0 is the only useful one for a precise measurement since D_0 is comparatively very small (its presence is due to centrifugal distortion of the molecule) and it cannot be found with high precision.

Typical of work in this field are the infra-red measurements of the absorption and emission spectra of carbon monoxide by Plyler, Blaine, and Connor [136] which, when combined with the microwave measurements of absorption in the same gas by Gilliam, Johnson, and Gordy [82] give a value for c of (299793 ± 6) km sec^{-1} (20 ppm). Earlier work using the same method gave values of (299776 ± 6) km sec^{-1} [142] (later revised to allow a greater uncertainty [140]), and (299789·8 ± 3) km sec^{-1} (10 ppm) [143]. The work of Rank, Guenther, Shearer, and Wiggins [141] on the spectrum of HCN gave a value for c of (299793·2 ± 1·8) km sec^{-1} (6 ppm). These measurements, using a method quite different in principle from the optical and microwave techniques of, for example, Bergstrand and Froome, provide valuable support for the results obtained by these workers.

3.6. The value of c

The 1955 reviews of the values of the physical constants by Cohen, DuMond, Rollet, and Layton [43] and by Bearden and Thomsen [17] suggested as the best value for c, $(299793\cdot0\pm0\cdot3)$ and $(299792\cdot8\pm0\cdot4)$ km sec^{-1} respectively. In 1956 Bergstrand [20] also suggested $(299793\cdot0\pm0\cdot3)$ km sec^{-1}, but in 1957 [23] revised his value, to take account of new geodimeter measurements, to $(299792\cdot9\pm0\cdot2)$ km sec^{-1}. In their review, Mulligan and McDonald [127] quote the value $(299792\cdot8\pm0\cdot6)$ km sec^{-1}, with limits which the authors admit to be generous. The reviewers quoted here took into account neither the corrected value [77] of Froome's 1954 measurement ($0\cdot25$ km sec^{-1} lower than was originally stated), nor Froome's 1958 [76] result of $(299792\cdot5\pm0\cdot1)$ km sec^{-1}. The latter is bound to carry considerable weight and it appears probable that the value of c is somewhat lower than the value which reviewers have so far deduced. Few experimenters, however, are likely to be troubled by an uncertainty of 1 part per million or so in the value of c.

3.7. Future measurements of c

The precision of the present day measurements of c is such that any attempt to reduce the errors appreciably would encounter the fundamental difficulty of the lack of availability of a suitable standard of length; this is particularly true in the optical measurements which use a baseline several kilometers long. A shortening of this baseline would involve the use of a higher modulation frequency if high precision were to be maintained. Modulation of a light beam at 300 Mc sec^{-1} has been reported by Rao and Murty [144] and at 2000 Mc sec^{-1} by Bömmel and Dransfeld [29] using diffraction from ultrasonic waves in quartz. A suggestion for the use of even higher effective modulation frequencies has been made by Sanders [154] but so far frequencies in this range have not been used to measure c. Their use, with the resultant shortening of the required baseline, may result in some increase of precision. Approaching the problem from the microwave point of view, the development of continuous wave sources of adequate power in the sub-millimeter range would lead to a reduction of some of the uncertainties in Froome's method, particularly if the measurement could be made in a vacuum. Janney has suggested [98] that the cavity resonator method is unlikely to give a precision better than 2 ppm because of the uncertainty in the properties of the surface of the cavity which makes the theoretical value of the correction uncertain. Essen's experimental elimination of the correction may, however, yield higher precision than this.

The establishment of the wavelength of an atomic transition as a fundamental standard of length, combined with the extremely high precision of present day frequency measurements, leads naturally to the idea of measuring simultaneously the wavelength and the frequency of an atomic transition in order to measure c. This method awaits the development of a direct method of measuring frequencies in the optical range by, for example, an extension of frequency multipliers from the microwave to the optical region.

If a technique of measuring c were developed which was capable of higher precision than could be achieved in defining a standard of length, its value as a method of measuring c would be lost because of the inadequacy of the length standard (see Appendix II.2). It would, however, then be possible to define a standard of length in terms of the constant c and a frequency. That is, a standard of length could be defined as the distance travelled by light in free space in a certain time, without knowing the value of c in terms of the present standard metre. The measurement of time interval or frequency is capable of greater precision by at least two orders of magnitude than the comparison of present length standards. Considerable improvement of the present techniques now used for measuring c would, however, be necessary, in order that such a length standard should be reproducible to a greater precision than is achievable in, say, the comparison of metre standards.

CHAPTER IV

RECENT PRECISE MEASUREMENTS

THE two groups of reviewers [17] [41] [43] [56] who have presented since 1950 tables of the best values of the atomic constants have used the values of a number of precisely measured quantities. Among these are three which are related to the magnetic dipole moment μ_p of the proton:

(i) the gyromagnetic ratio of the proton, γ_p;

(ii) the proton magnetic moment in nuclear magnetons, μ_p/μ_N;

(iii) the proton magnetic moment in Bohr magnetons μ_p/μ_0; where $\mu_N = he/4\pi Mc$ is the nuclear magneton (M = mass of proton) and $\mu_0 = he/4\pi mc$ is the Bohr magneton. The measurement of these quantities by radiofrequency techniques was made possible by the development in 1946 of methods of detecting so-called 'proton resonance'.

The phenomenon of nuclear resonance, which may be observed for all nuclei whose spin is not zero, is readily observable in the case of the proton, which has spin $\frac{1}{2}$ and a comparatively large magnetic moment (2·79 nm). In a magnetic field H a proton has two quantum states parallel and antiparallel to the field; the states are separated in energy by $2\mu_p H$. The protons are, in practice, usually those contained in a sample of hydrogeneous liquid such as water or mineral oil (liquid paraffin) at room temperature. The sample is placed in the steady magnetic field and a coil is arranged to produce a small alternating field of frequency ν at right angles to the steady field. When ν is close to or equal to the value

$$\nu_n = 2\mu_p H/h \tag{4.1}$$

it will cause transitions between the proton's two energy states. In thermal equilibrium there are in the sample slightly more protons in the lower state than the upper (the ratio is $e^{2\mu_p H/kT}$ where $2\mu_p H/kT$ is commonly between 10^{-8} and 10^{-4}) and since the probabilities of transitions up and down are equally likely the observation of the net absorption relies on this small population difference. The frequency is about $4 \cdot 2$ Mc sec^{-1} in a field of 10^3 gauss, so, in the usual range of fields used in the laboratory, lies between a few kc sec^{-1} and, say, 100 Mc sec^{-1}. Resonance may be detected in several different ways, of which one is the net absorption of energy from the coil producing the alternating field.

The relation $\nu_n = (2\mu_p/h)H$ indicates that there is a fundamental relation between ν_n and H. The quantity $(4\pi\mu_p/h)$, the ratio of the magnetic moment to the angular momentum of the proton, is called the gyromagnetic ratio of the proton γ_p, and it may obviously be measured by a comparison of ν_n and H. The narrow width of the absorption lines observed in proton resonance using liquid samples make it a particularly attractive method of measuring γ_p, and once γ_p is known, of measuring magnetic fields in terms of ν_n. In a water or oil sample the field H at the proton is not quite equal to the externally applied field because of the diamagnetic effect of the electrons in the molecules, and also because of the susceptibility of the sample as a whole. The correction for these effects is small and calculable.

The brief description of proton resonance given above has been in terms of a quantum picture; it is often preferable to visualize the motion of the protons in classical terms, in which case ν_n is the Larmor frequency of precession about the field direction of the protons considered as elementary spinning magnets.

4.1. The gyromagnetic ratio of the proton

Three measurements of γ_p have been made: by Thomas, Driscoll, and Hipple at the National Bureau of Standards, Washington, D.C. in 1950 [170], by Kirchner and Wilhelmy at Cologne University in 1957 [107] [188] and by Driscoll and Bender at the National Bureau of Standards in 1958 [52].

The earliest of these measurements was made before proton resonance in weak fields had been detected. Consequently it was necessary to use a proton resonance frequency of 20 Mc sec^{-1}, which corresponds to a field of about 4770 gauss.

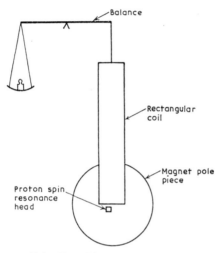

FIG. 8. Thomas, Driscoll, and Hipple's apparatus for measuring the gyromagnetic ratio of the proton.

A field of this magnitude necessitated the use of an electro-magnet; the magnet used had a gap 2″ wide between polepieces 12½″ in diameter and its field was stabilized against a fixed frequency of 20 Mc sec^{-1} by using the proton resonance phenomenon. The magnet was set up with its pole faces vertical and the field strength near the centre of the gap was measured by weighing the force on a 9-turn coil wound on the edge of a precisely made rectangular glass former 10 cm wide by 70 cm high carrying a known current (Fig. 8). This coil was suspended from one arm of a conventional balance, and had the centre of one of its horizontal edges at the centre of the magnet; the other horizontal edge was outside the magnet, where the field was small and known sufficiently well for a correction to be made. In this way the value of the field was

measured in terms of the absolute ampere (see Appendix II.4),
the value of the acceleration due to gravity and the dimensions
of the coil. The proton resonance frequency at points near the
centre of the magnet gap was also measured, and from the
results a value of γ_p was deduced.

Wilhelmy placed a proton resonance sample in a field of

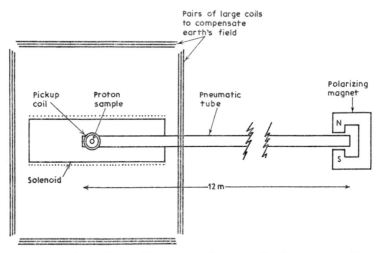

FIG. 9. Bender and Driscoll's apparatus for measuring the gyromagnetic
ratio of the proton.

about 100 gauss produced by a solenoid wound on a water-
cooled brass former 100 cm long and 6 cm in diameter. His
result disagrees with the other two determinations and is not
consistent with other atomic constants. It is generally thought
that the discrepancy is due to the electrical standards used by
Wilhelmy, or to the presence of magnetic contamination in his
apparatus which gave a field strength at the proton sample
different from the value calculated from the solenoid dimensions and the current.

Driscoll and Bender's determination of γ_p has a reported
uncertainty of less than 10 ppm. A magnetic field of about
12 gauss was produced by passing a known current through a
solenoid of known dimensions (Fig. 9). The former of the
solenoid was a massive fused silica tube 100 cm long and 28 cm

diameter in which a spiral groove was cut to receive a single layer of copper wire. The spin resonance frequency of the proton in the field was measured by using the method of free precession [85] [132]. The details, and the explanation of the method in classical terms, are as follows: a proton sample, either pure water or benzene, contained in a spherical bulb 2 cm in diameter was first placed in a steady field of 5000 gauss at a place about 12 m away from the solenoid, so that, at the solenoid, the effect of leakage field from the magnet used was negligible. The effect of this strong field was to increase the Boltzmann factor $e^{(2\mu_p H/kT)}$ to many times the value it would have in the weak field of the solenoid. Once polarized in this way, the sample retained its polarization for several seconds. It was shot pneumatically into the centre of the solenoid; on its way from the magnet to the solenoid the polarization of the sample aligned itself along the instantaneous direction of the field. The protons were then set precessing about the solenoid field by applying a short pulse of alternating magnetic field, perpendicular to the solenoid field, at a frequency roughly equal to the precession frequency, 52·5 kc sec^{-1}, and of the correct duration to produce a 90° change of direction. The protons were then left to precess freely about the solenoid field, gradually giving up their energy to the atoms in the liquid as they became more and more aligned with the field. As they did so, they induced a small signal in a pickup coil surrounding the sample, and the frequency of this signal was measured. A signal could be observed for about 3 sec in water, and for 18 sec in benzene, allowing a very precise measurement of the frequency. The experiment was done in an isolated hut at Fredericksburg Magnetic Observatory, remote from man-made magnetic disturbances. The component of the earth's field perpendicular to the axis of the solenoid was cancelled out by using large coils, and the component parallel to the axis was eliminated by taking frequency measurements with the solenoid current reversed. The diurnal fluctuations of the earth's field were troublesome at certain times of day. A preliminary result of this experiment has been published so far; the final value awaits measurements of the pitch of the solenoid winding, but it is unlikely to differ appreciably from the result available at present. Most of the uncertainty in the result of this experiment comes from the determination, using a current balance, of the solenoid current in terms of the absolute ampere.

The results of the three measurements of γ_p are:

Thomas, Driscoll, and Hipple 1950:
  $(2\cdot67530\pm0\cdot00006)\times10^4$ rad sec^{-1} gauss^{-1} (22 ppm)

Kirchner and Wilhelmy 1957:
  $(2\cdot67556\pm0\cdot00008)\times10^4$ rad sec^{-1} gauss^{-1} (30 ppm)

Driscoll and Bender 1958:
  $(2\cdot67520\pm0\cdot00002)\times10^4$ rad sec^{-1} gauss^{-1} (7·5 ppm)

It is generally agreed that Kirchner and Wilhemy's result must be disregarded. The lack of agreement between the other two results is a matter of some concern, especially as the evaluation of magnetic field strengths in terms of ν_n relies on this figure.

4.2. The proton magnetic moment in nuclear magnetons

The quantity μ_p/μ_N may be found by the comparison of the spin resonance frequency ν_n and the cyclotron frequency ν_c of protons in the same magnetic field H, a method first suggested by Alvarez and Bloch [1]. The cyclotron frequency ν_c is equal to $eH/2\pi Mc$, so from (4.1) above,

$$\frac{\nu_n}{\nu_c} = \frac{2\mu_p H/h}{eH/(2\pi Mc)} = \frac{\mu_p}{\left(\dfrac{he}{4\pi Mc}\right)} = \frac{\mu_p}{\mu_N} \qquad (4.2)$$

The cyclotron frequency could, in principle, be measured by finding the resonance condition in a conventional type of cyclotron structure situated in a uniform magnetic field. In practice it is preferable to modify the apparatus slightly to obtain a more precise determination of ν_c.

At the National Bureau of Standards Sommer, Thomas, and Hipple [164] constructed a small proton accelerator, the

'omegatron', Fig. 10, in which the final orbit radius was 1 cm
and the steady magnetic field strength was about 4770 gauss.
Instead of accelerating the protons with 'dees', as in the
cyclotron, which gives a fixed energy gain of $2Ve$ per revolution,

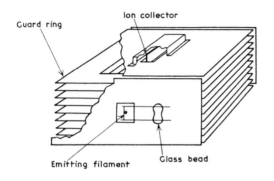

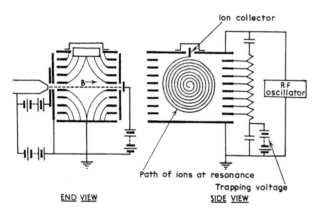

Fig. 10. The omegatron of Sommer, Thomas, and Hipple for measuring
the cyclotron frequency of protons and other ions.

where V is the instantaneous potential difference across the
dees, a uniform alternating field was used, produced by the
frame-like electrodes. The energy gain per revolution was thus
proportional to the radius, and initially very small. In this
way the protons made a very large number of revolutions
before striking a collector placed near the outside of the
electrode structure. This gave very narrow resonance peaks

(about 1 part in 35,000 wide at half-maximum) as the frequency of the accelerating potential was varied. The protons were produced, as in the early cyclotrons, by passing a narrow beam of electrons through the centre of the electrodes, of sufficient energy to ionize the hydrogen present in the apparatus at a pressure of about 10^{-7} mm Hg. The protons were prevented from drifting in a direction parallel to the magnetic field by applying a small (0·1 volt) positive bias, the 'trapping' voltage, to the RF electrodes. The proton spin resonance frequency was measured in the same magnetic field by substituting for the omegatron a proton sample (water).

The presence of an outwardly directed static radial electric field E_r at the orbit of an ion of mass M_i alters the cyclotron frequency of that ion from the value $\nu_c = (eH/2\pi M_i c)$ to the value

$$\nu'_c = \nu_c \left(1 - \frac{M_i \langle E_r \rangle}{H^2 er}\right) \qquad (4.3)$$

where r is the orbit radius and $\langle E_r \rangle$ is the average value of E_r round the orbit, i.e.

$$\langle E_r \rangle = \frac{1}{2\pi} \int_0^{2\pi} E_r \, d\theta, \qquad (4.4)$$

in which θ defines the azimuthal position of the ion relative to the centre of the orbit in a stationary frame of reference. The expression 4.3 holds only for $|(\nu - \nu_c)/\nu_c| \ll 1$, which is generally the case in practice.

In the omegatron a steady radial field E_r was present, due partly to the trapping voltage and to a smaller extent to the space charge of the ions within the omegatron. The effect of this field was eliminated by making measurements of ν_c for ions of different masses under identical conditions. The ions used were H^+, H_2^+, D_2^+, and H_2O^+, which have identical charges, and masses of M and approximately $2M$, $4M$, and $18M$ respectively. By assuming that $\langle E_r \rangle$ remained the same it was possible to use expression 4.3 to extrapolate to zero mass and thus eliminate the correction due to the unknown field $\langle E_r \rangle$. The exact values of M_i had to be used to deduce the proton cyclotron frequency from the observed values of the cyclotron frequencies of the ions used. The values of M_i are known, with very small errors, from mass spectrographic measurements. Sommer, Thomas, and Hipple quoted as their result $\mu_p = (2\cdot792765 \pm 0\cdot00006)$ nuclear magnetons (21 ppm).

At Stanford University, California, Jeffries [99] in 1951 measured μ_p/μ_N by the use of a small cyclotron (Fig. 11), with conventional electrodes, arranged to decelerate rather than accelerate protons. Used in this way the cyclotron could be

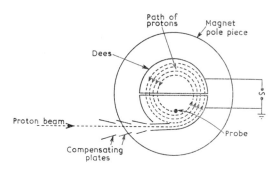

FIG. 11. Jeffries' inverse cyclotron.

operated with an alternating potential applied to the dees near the nth harmonic of the cyclotron frequency, where n is an odd integer. The observed resonance peaks have a fractional frequency width $\Delta\nu_c/\nu_c$ which is inversely proportional to n, and the resolution is correspondingly improved. Jeffries detected resonance at the ninth harmonic of ν_c by observing the proton current collected by a probe near the centre of the dees. The protons were generated externally in an ion source and were injected at an energy of about 20 keV into the dees after passing between a series of electrodes which produced an electric field perpendicular to the direction of motion of the protons to compensate for the magnetic force on them as they entered the magnet.

The interpretation of the cyclotron resonance peaks observed in an apparatus of this sort is not straightforward. Jeffries' original result $\mu_p = (2\cdot7924 \pm 0\cdot0002)$ nuclear magnetons (70 ppm) was not in good agreement with that of Sommer,

Thomas, and Hipple, but subsequent work by Trigger [175] in 1956, using essentially the same apparatus as Jeffries and a more detailed theoretical analysis of the results gave a value $\mu_p = (2\cdot79275 \pm 0\cdot00010)$ nuclear magnetons (36 ppm).

At the Clarendon Laboratory, Oxford, Collington, Dellis, Sanders, and Turberfield [44][155] used a modified form of the inverted cyclotron to measure μ_p/μ_N. The electrodes had a parallel sided central section and, on either side, a 'dee' similar

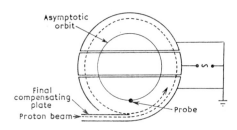

FIG. 12. The Oxford modification of the inverse cyclotron.

to the cyclotron (Fig. 12). Protons were injected tangentially near the outside of these electrodes in a manner resembling that used by Jeffries. Between the central conductor and the dees was applied an alternating potential at a frequency close to an even harmonic of the cyclotron frequency. Those injected protons which crossed the central conductor in the appropriate phase received a net deceleration at each pair of gaps, but as they moved inwards they approached a radius at which the time taken to cross the central conductor was just one cycle of the alternating voltage, which is the condition for no net change of energy. In this way the protons described a large number of revolutions at a large radius where their energies were still high. The magnetic field was 2350 gauss $(\nu_n = 10$ Mc sec$^{-1})$ and the eighth harmonic of ν_c ($8 \times 3\cdot58$ Mc sec^{-1}) was used. In 1955 these workers quoted $\mu_p = (2\cdot79281 \pm 0\cdot00004)$ nuclear magnetons (14 ppm). Later, after a more extensive set of measurements using H$^+$ and H$_2^+$ ions at both the eighth and sixteenth harmonics of ν_c, and after a more rigorous theoretical analysis of the motion of ions in such a structure, they revised their result to $\mu_p = (2\cdot79277\pm0\cdot00005)$ nuclear magnetons (18 ppm).

Omitting the early results obtained by the inverted cyclotron methods, the values which have been quoted for μ_p/μ_N are as follows:

Sommer, Thomas, and Hipple, 1951.
$\quad$ $\mu_p = (2\cdot792765\pm0\cdot00006)$ nuclear magnetons (21 ppm).

Trigger, 1956.
$\quad$ $\mu_p = (2\cdot79275\pm0\cdot00010)$ nuclear magnetons (36 ppm).

Dellis, Sanders, and Turberfield, 1959.
$\quad$ $\mu_p = (2\cdot79277\pm0\cdot00005)$ nuclear magnetons (18 ppm).

In all these measurements the determination of the proton cyclotron frequency presents the most difficulty. Not only is there the possibility, discussed above, that static radial electric fields disturb the cyclotron frequency, but in all three cases the ions move in a changing electric field due to the radiofrequency voltage applied to the electrodes. This distorts the resonance peak, and the deduction of the true cyclotron frequency from the observed peak is by no means straightforward. In spite of the apparent good agreement of the results a systematic error due to this effect may well exist.

4.3. The proton magnetic moment in Bohr magnetons

The ratio of the spin resonance frequency of protons, ν_n, to the cyclotron frequency of electrons, ν_e, measured in the same magnetic field, may be shown (see 4.2) to be equal to the proton magnetic moment in Bohr magnetons, i.e.

$$\frac{\nu_n}{\nu_e} = \frac{\mu_p}{\left(\dfrac{he}{4\pi mc}\right)} = \frac{\mu_p}{\mu_0} \qquad (4.5)$$

where μ_0 is the Bohr magneton. Because the Bohr magneton is a larger unit than the nuclear magneton in the ratio M/m ($= 1836$ approximately) the ratio of the two frequencies is correspondingly smaller. Experimenters have chosen so far to use a value of ν_n of the same order of magnitude as that used in the proton cyclotron frequency measurements, i.e. 15 Mc sec^{-1}, which places the electron cyclotron frequency in the region of 10 kMc sec^{-1}, where oscillators and waveguide components are readily available. The advantage of using a high value of the electron cyclotron frequency is apparent from the fact that the resolution $\nu_e/\Delta\nu_e$ obtained in measuring ν_e depends on the number of revolutions n an electron makes in the field before it is lost; in fact $\nu_e/\Delta\nu_e$ is approximately equal to n. In order to obtain a resolution of, say, 10^5 using a value of $\nu_e = 10^{10}$ c sec^{-1}, it is necessary for the electron to exist in the field for the order of 10^{-5} sec. Since the translational velocity of an electron having an energy of only 1 eV is about 5×10^7 cm sec^{-1} it is obvious that very low energy electrons have to be used. Any attempt to confine the electrons by the use of inhomogeneous electric or magnetic fields would lead to a disastrous shift or a broadening of the observed cyclotron frequency.

The experiment performed by Gardner and Purcell [79] [80] at Harvard University used a magnetic field of about 3300 gauss ($\nu_n = 14\cdot24$ Mc sec^{-1}) and the electron cyclotron frequency was close to 9·4 kMc sec^{-1}. Electrons were generated at a hot cathode (Fig. 13), passed through small slits in opposite sides of an evacuated copper waveguide and were collected at an electrode on the far side of the waveguide. The electrons, which are ejected from the cathode with an approximately Maxwellian distribution of velocities, were accelerated by holding the cathode at a small negative potential V_a with respect to the body of the waveguide. The uniform magnetic field was parallel to the line which passed from cathode to collector through the centre of the slits. The electrons were ejected from the cathode with small components of velocity perpendicular to the field direction, and so moved in helical paths of very small radius with the magnetic lines of force as the axes of the helices. Down the waveguide passed electromagnetic radiation at a frequency ν_e in the TE$_{10}$ mode, and the guide was arranged so that the oscillating electric field was perpendicular to the steady magnetic field. The waveguide was terminated by a reflecting copper wall one quarter wavelength beyond the slits, so that the electrons passed through an antinode of the electric field. Under these conditions the radii of their helical paths increased, and the electrons gained energy from the electromagnetic field when ν was close to ν_e. It was expected that this would cause a dip in the collector current as ν was varied through ν_e,

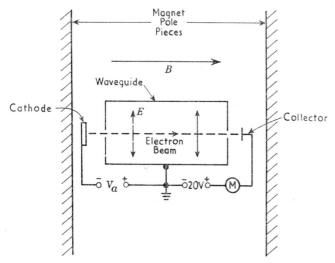

FIG. 13. Gardner and Purcell's apparatus for measuring the cyclotron frequency of electrons.

since electrons moving in a path of sufficiently large radius would not pass through the second slit. A rather broad dip in the collector current was observed when V_a was greater than 3 V, corresponding to a resolution of about 1 part in 650. When V_a was less than 3 V a much sharper rise in current was superimposed on the dip, giving a resolution about ten times better. This rise was attributed to a reduction of the space charge density due to the slow moving electrons in the waveguide (since these were the ones whose orbits expand most) and the consequent increase in the space charge limited current of faster moving electrons. The latter spent a very short time in the waveguide and consequently their orbits remained small enough in radius to pass through the second slit, thus giving an indication of the resonance of the slow electrons. A very small electron current (less than 5×10^{-10} A) was used and the shift of the cyclotron frequency due to the space charge in the beam was estimated to be negligible. The proton spin resonance frequency was measured by substituting a proton sample for the waveguide before and after each determination of ν_e. A correction for the magnetic field produced by the cathode heater current was made by reversing the current and averaging positions of the observed electron resonance peaks. There were, however, certain unexplained shifts of the position of the resonance peaks when the cathode potential was varied.

Subsequent workers have abandoned the detection of electron cyclotron resonance by effects dependent on the physical increase in the orbit size, and have detected instead the absorption of power from the electromagnetic field as an indication of resonance. Franken and Liebes [73] at Stanford University measured the absorption of power due to cyclotron resonance in a highly evacuated bulb containing photoelectrons ejected from an illuminated potassium film on the inner side of the bulb. An appreciable space charge density was built up inside the bulb and a correction to the observed cyclotron frequency was necessary, as indicated in equation (4.3). This correction was eliminated by measuring ν_e' at different values of H, ranging from 750 to 1700 gauss. By plotting ν_e' against $1/H^2$ and extrapolating to $1/H^2 = 0$ the value of ν_e could be found; it was assumed that the electric field distribution within the bulb was independent of H. A linear dependence of ν_e' on $1/H^2$ was found within very narrow limits; the slope of the line depended on the sample and the way in which it was illuminated. The Pyrex glass bulb was about 5 mm inside diameter and was placed in a cavity tuneable from 2 to 4·5 kMc sec^{-1}.

A mineral oil proton sample could be interchanged with the bulb to measure ν_n. A total of 42 different extrapolations were made, using a total of 279 data points. The intercepts at

$1/H^2 = 0$ showed an overall spread of about 1 part in 30,000 and the final result, taking into account various other sources of uncertainty, was quoted with a probable error of 4·5 ppm.

The measurement of μ_p/μ_0 has been continued at Harvard University by Hardy and Purcell [87]. Basically the apparatus was similar to that used by Gardner and Purcell, but the resonant absorption of microwave energy by the electrons was detected. The proton resonance frequency was increased to 20 Mc sec^{-1}, and a very low noise microwave receiver was used to detect electron cyclotron resonance. Electrons, generated at a heated cathode, were admitted with low energy into a cavity tuned to the microwave frequency (about 13·5 kMc sec^{-1}). The potential distribution in the cavity could be varied slightly by altering the potential of the external electrodes. Electrons ejected normally from the cathode with an energy eV were brought to rest at a place where the potential was $-V$ with respect to a point just outside the cathode surface. This point could be arranged to lie within the cavity; the time spent in the cavity by these particular electrons could be arranged to be sufficiently long to give a very narrow cyclotron resonance peak, less than 1 part in 10^5 wide. A power of only 10^{-14}–10^{-15} watts was supplied to the cavity, and the maximum energy gained by the electrons was less than 0·05 eV, so that relativistic increase of mass was negligible. The magnetic field varied by about 6 parts in 10^6 over the cavity, so it was important to arrange to record only the resonances which took place at the centre of the cavity. To ascertain when this was so, a small coil was arranged with its axis perpendicular to the main magnetic field and passing through the centre of the cavity. When the current was switched on through this coil only those resonances which occurred at the centre of the cavity were unchanged in position, since only at this point was the field due to the coil perpendicular to the main field, and consequently the change in total field was negligible. The proton spin resonance frequency was measured by placing a water sample at the centre of the cavity.

The following is a summary of the results for μ_p/μ_0:

Gardner and Purcell, 1949.

$\mu_p = (1\cdot52101\pm0\cdot00002)\times10^{-3}$ Bohr magnetons (13 ppm)

Franken and Liebes, 1957.

$\mu_p = (1\cdot521047\pm0\cdot000007)\times10^{-3}$ Bohr magnetons (4·5 ppm)

Hardy and Purcell, 1959.

$\mu_p = (1\cdot521032\pm0\cdot000003)\times10^{-3}$ Bohr magnetons (2 ppm)

As in the measurements of μ_p/μ_N discussed in the preceding section there may still, in spite of the care taken by the experimenters, be an undiscovered source of systematic error present. Again radial electric field components must be suspected. Care was taken to eliminate their effect in the Franken and Liebes experiment, but there remains the assumption that the electric field was independent of the steady magnetic field.

4.4. The ratio of the electron magnetic moment and the proton magnetic moment

The magnetic moment of the electron μ_e differs from one Bohr magneton μ_0 by an amount which is known from the theory of quantum electrodynamics [102] [135] [157] [165] to be given by

$$\mu_e = \mu_0\left(1 + \frac{\alpha}{2\pi} - 0\cdot328\frac{\alpha^2}{\pi^2}\right) = 1\cdot0011596\mu_0 \qquad (4.6)$$

where the numerical value has been obtained by substituting for the fine structure constant α the value $7\cdot2972\times10^{-3}$. There seems little reason to doubt the validity of this theoretical relation, so by its use a measurement of (μ_p/μ_e) is equivalent to one of (μ_p/μ_0). As it turns out, the former can be measured to a far higher precision than the latter, so that the measurements of (μ_p/μ_0) described in section 4.3 are in fact of little importance in evaluating the constants, but provide an experimental verification of relation 4.6 above.

The ratio (μ_p/μ_e) has been measured by the investigation of the Zeeman effect of the hyperfine structure of the ground state of the hydrogen atom by two distinct methods, one involving an atomic beam technique and the other the absorption of energy in a microwave cavity. The levels of the $1^2S_{\frac{1}{2}}$ ground state of hydrogen are shown in Fig. 14. The magnetic moment of the proton causes the energy difference

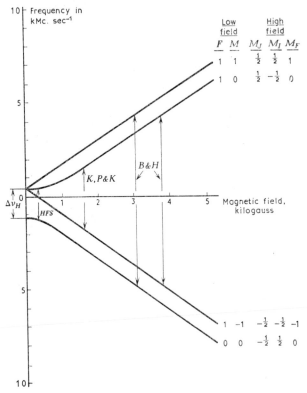

FIG. 14. The Zeeman effect of the hyperfine levels of the ground state $1^2S_{\frac{1}{2}}$ of hydrogen.

(expressed in frequency units) $\Delta\nu_H$ in zero applied magnetic field. When a field is applied the two levels split as shown into four. These levels can be described in a low field, in which the nuclear and electronic momenta are coupled, by the quantum number $\mathbf{F} = \mathbf{I} + \mathbf{J}$ (where $\mathbf{I}$ is the nuclear spin and $\mathbf{J}$ is the total electronic angular momentum), and its associated magnetic quantum number M. In a field high enough to decouple **I** and **J** the levels are described by the magnetic quantum numbers M_I, M_J, and $M_F = M_I + M_J$. The energy of the levels at any magnetic field strength H is given by the Breit–Rabi expression [31]

$$W_{F,M_F} = -\frac{h\Delta\nu_{\mathrm{H}}}{4} - 2\mu_p M_F H \pm \frac{h\Delta\nu_{\mathrm{H}}}{2}(1 + 2M_F x + x^2)^{\frac{1}{2}} \quad (4.7)$$

where
$$x = 2(\mu_J + \mu_p)H/(h\Delta\nu_{\mathrm{H}}) \quad (4.8)$$

In (4.6) the positive sign is taken when $\mathbf{F} = 1$ and the negative sign when $\mathbf{F} = 0$. In (4.8) μ_J is the total electronic magnetic moment and both it and μ_p are taken to be positive. In the ground state of hydrogen the electronic moment μ_J is due to electron spin only. The moment μ'_e of the electron bound in the atom is related to the moment μ_e of the free electron by the expression [125]

$$\mu'_e = \mu_e\left(1 - \frac{\alpha^2}{3} + \dots\right) \quad (4.9)$$

in which the relativistic correction factor $\left(1 - \dfrac{\alpha^2}{3}\right)$ differs from unity by approximately 18 ppm.

It is evident that a measurement of the difference in energy ΔW between two levels described by (4.7), together with a knowledge of the values of (a) H in terms of the proton magnetic moment (i.e. $H = h\nu_n/2\mu_p$, see page 37), (b) the value of $\Delta\nu_{\mathrm{H}}$ and (c) the correction factor in (4.9), are sufficient to establish the relation between μ_p and μ_e. The hyperfine splitting $\Delta\nu_{\mathrm{H}}$ has been measured with very high precision (see next section) and the proton spin resonance frequency ν_n is measured by conventional techniques using an oil or water sample. The precision of the experiment is high enough so that the uncertainty of the magnitude of the correction to the observed values of ν_p due to the diamagnetic susceptibility of the sample sets the limit of the precision of the experiment, and the results are usually quoted in terms of μ'_p, the observed value of μ_p in the sample used.

The atomic beam method [139] using a beam of hydrogen atoms generated in a Wood discharge tube, has been used by

Koenig, Prodell, and Kusch [108] at Columbia University, New York, to detect the transition labelled K, P & K in Fig. 14. The transition frequency $(= (W_{1,0} - W_{1,-1})/h)$ was 3655 Mc sec^{-1} and the magnetic field strength H was in the region of 1500 gauss. Their published result was

$$\mu_e/\mu'_p = 657 \cdot 2288 \pm 0 \cdot 0004 \ (0 \cdot 6 \text{ ppm})$$

where μ'_p is the value of μ_p obtained before making the correction for the diamagnetism of the proton sample.

A different technique for observing the transitions was used by Beringer and Heald [24] at Yale University. The hydrogen atoms were introduced into a TE$_{011}$ cavity, tuned to about 9000 Mc sec^{-1}, by passing a Wood discharge tube through the cavity. The cavity was placed between the poles of an electromagnet and the two transitions labelled B & H (Fig. 14) were observed by the resonant absorption of microwave energy from the cavity when the magnetic field was varied and the frequency of the microwave energy supplied to the cavity from a klystron was kept fixed. The net absorption of energy was due to a small Boltzmann population difference between the upper and lower Zeeman levels. Beringer and Heald's result was

$$\frac{\mu_e}{\mu'_p} = 658 \cdot 2298 \pm 0 \cdot 0003 \ (0 \cdot 45 \text{ ppm})$$

The difference between the two results is larger than their combined quoted errors, but the precision of both experiments is so high that, for the purpose of deriving the values of the constants, the lack of agreement is immaterial. As is discussed in more detail in Chapter V, the quantity (μ_e/μ_p) appears in conjunction with (μ_p/μ_N), the value of which has a much greater experimental uncertainty.

4.5. The hyperfine separation in the ground state of hydrogen

The quantity $\Delta\nu_{\mathrm{H}}$ (Fig. 14) appears in equation (4.7) and a knowledge of its value is necessary to derive (μ_e/μ_p). It has been measured by essentially the same techniques as described in the preceding section, but using the transition marked HFS in a very small magnetic field (of the order of 0·1 to 1 gauss).

The effect of a small magnetic field on the frequency of the (1, 0–0, 0) transition (where the numerals denote the initial and final values of F, M) is of second order only, and the correction to zero field can be found sufficiently well by making less precise measurements of the (1, 1–0, 0) and (1, −1–1, 0) transitions. The atomic beam method was used by Prodell and Kusch [138], and later by Kusch [110] who obtained the result

$$\Delta\nu_\mathrm{H} = (1420 \cdot 40573 \pm 0 \cdot 00005) \ \mathrm{Mc} \ \mathrm{sec}^{-1} \ (0 \cdot 035 \ \mathrm{ppm})$$

A method similar to that of Beringer and Heald for the determination of (μ_e/μ_p) was used by Wittke and Dicke [191] to measure $\Delta\nu_\mathrm{H}$. They quoted the value

$$\Delta\nu_\mathrm{H} = (1420 \cdot 40580 \pm 0 \cdot 00008) \ \mathrm{Mc} \ \mathrm{sec}^{-1} \ (0 \cdot 055 \ \mathrm{ppm})$$

The result of Prodell and Kusch is essentially in agreement with this, and the precision is ample for the purpose of the derivation of the value of (μ_e/μ_p) as described in the preceding section.

These measurements of the hyperfine separation of the ground state of hydrogen have been made to a very high precision (the order of 0·05 ppm). Unfortunately this high precision cannot be utilized directly in the evaluation of the constants because some of the factors in the theoretical expression for $\Delta\nu_\mathrm{H}$ are of uncertain magnitude. At the moment the value of $\Delta\nu_\mathrm{H}$ is only of importance in evaluating (μ_e/μ_p) which, as discussed above, has to be used with the value of (μ_p/μ_N), and its associated rather large uncertainty, in the derivation of the constants.

4.6. The fine structure of deuterium

The frequency separation $\Delta\nu_\mathrm{D}$ of the $2\mathrm{P}_{\frac{1}{2}}$ and the $2\mathrm{P}_{\frac{3}{2}}$ levels in deuterium is a quantity which can both be expressed in terms of some of the fundamental constants and be measured experimentally with high precision. The $n = 2$ states of the hydrogen or deuterium atom are shown in Fig. 15 as a function of magnetic field and are labelled according to Lamb's original notation.

The derivation of the theoretical expression for $\Delta \nu_D$ and the measurement of this quantity was part of a programme undertaken by Lamb and his collaborators at Columbia University. The main success of this work was the prediction

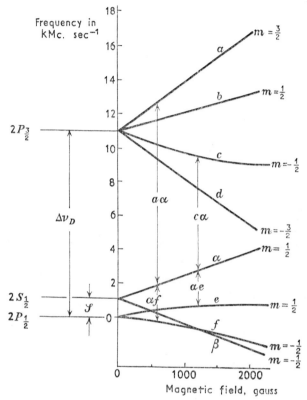

FIG. 15. The fine structure of the $n = 2$ levels of hydrogen and deuterium.

and experimental verification of the 'Lamb shift', the frequency difference $\mathscr{S}$ between the $2S_{\frac{1}{2}}$ and $2P_{\frac{1}{2}}$ states of the hydrogen atom which had previously, in the light of the Dirac theory, been thought to be degenerate. Up to 1947, no experiment had been devised which gave definite evidence that such a separation existed. Using a radiofrequency spectroscopic method at frequencies of about 2 kMc sec^{-1} Lamb and Retherford showed that the shift existed and subsequently they, and later Lamb, Treibwasser, and Dayhoff, measured both the Lamb shift $\mathscr{S}$ and the fine structure separation $\Delta\nu_D$ in hydrogen and deuterium with high precision [48] [112] [174].

Their apparatus, shown diagrammatically in Fig. 16 was contained between the poles of an electromagnet. A beam

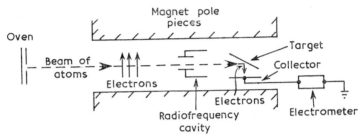

FIG. 16. The apparatus used by Lamb *et al.* for the deuterium fine structure experiment.

containing about 64 per cent of atomic hydrogen or deuterium was produced by dissociating the molecular gas in a tungsten tube heated to 2500°K and allowing the gas to emerge from a system of collimating slits. The atoms were then excited to the $n = 2$ state (10·2 eV above the ground state) by a stream of electrons moving across the beam at an energy of about 13·5 eV, which was found to be the most effective value. The excited atoms then passed through a radiofrequency field where transitions between the various Zeeman levels could be induced; this field was produced by a coaxial resonator of appropriate design. The detection of resonance depended on the fact that the $2S_{\frac{1}{2}}$ state is metastable, since transitions from it to the ground state are forbidden ($\Delta l = 0$) and spontaneous transitions to lower lying $2P_{\frac{1}{2}}$ levels are very unlikely because of the small energy difference. If a transition is induced from the metastable $2S_{\frac{1}{2}}$ state to one of the P states the atom decays to the ground state within about 10^{-8} sec; in the atomic beam the atom moved only a few thousandths of a millimetre in this time. The metastable atoms in the beam were detected by allowing them to fall on a tungsten target. In giving up their excitation energy at the target they ejected electrons from it which were collected by another plate. Any decrease in the number of metastable atoms resulted in a decrease of the collector current. Transitions from the Zeeman components of the $2S_{\frac{1}{2}}$ state caused by the radio-frequency field of the cavity showed up in this way.

The experiment was done by keeping the frequency of the supply to the cavity fixed and varying the magnetic field. The field strength was measured in the early experiments by a rotating coil and later by a proton resonance probe. The transitions used to measure $(\Delta\nu_D - \mathscr{S})$ [48] were those marked $a\alpha$ and $c\alpha$, and those marked αe and αf were used to measure $\mathscr{S}$ [174]. Two different values of the frequency, and consequently two values of the magnetic field, were used in both cases; in the former the frequencies were 7195 and 10795 Mc sec^{-1}, and in the latter 2195 and 2395 Mc sec^{-1}. The values corresponding to zero field were then found by extrapolation, knowing the equations of the levels as a function of magnetic field [111]. The resonances observed with the metastable atom detector had a width corresponding to about 100 Mc sec^{-1}, owing to the short lifetime (10^{-8} sec) of the P state. The symmetrical form of the resonances made it possible to measure their position to better than 0·1 Mc sec^{-1}. So far no mention of the hyperfine splitting of the levels, owing to the nuclear spin and magnetic moment, has been made; although it is too small to show in the diagram it is nevertheless just detectable in the measurement of the fine structure separation. The hyperfine splitting of the $n = 2$ levels is much smaller than that of the ground state, and is smaller in deuterium than in hydrogen because of the small magnetic moment of the deuteron (0·86 nm compared with 2·79 nm for the proton). For this latter reason the measurement of the deuterium fine structure is used in the derivation of the values of the atomic constants.

The theoretical expression for the fine structure separation in deuterium is

$$\Delta\nu_D = \frac{\alpha^2 R_D c}{16}\left[1 + \frac{5}{8}\alpha^2 + \frac{\alpha}{\pi}\left(1 - 5\cdot946\frac{\alpha}{\pi}\right)\right] \qquad (4.10)$$

plus higher order terms which are negligible. In this expression

α is the fine structure constant $(2\pi e^2/hc)$, and R_D is the Rydberg constant for deuterium. The first two terms are contained in the Dirac theory and the last two are the result of the quantum electrodynamic correction which also accounts for the Lamb shift $\mathscr{S}$ and for the fact that the magnetic moment of the electron is slightly greater than one Bohr magneton. The result of the measurements of Dayhoff, Triebwasser, and Lamb gave

$$\Delta\nu_D = 10971{\cdot}59 \pm 0{\cdot}20 \text{ Mc sec}^{-1} \text{ (20 ppm)}$$

In the above expression (4.10) the values of R_D and c are known to a far higher precision than is $\Delta\nu_D$, so that the measured value of $\Delta\nu_D$ can be used to calculate a value for α, the fine structure constant. It is this quantity, derived from the measurement of $\Delta\nu_D$, which is used in the evaluation of the fundamental constants. The high precision with which $\Delta\nu_D$ has been measured make it a valuable contribution to our knowledge of the values of the constants. The main contribution to the uncertainty of the measurement arises from the lifetime of the P-state. Any experiment aimed at higher precision would have to overcome this fundamental limitation. It is unlikely that any improvement could be achieved by an experiment which was, in principle, a repetition of that of Lamb and his collaborators.

4.7. The mass of the proton

A quantity which appears in connection with the derivation of the constants from the measurements described in this chapter is the mass of the proton. In some respects, of course, the mass of the proton itself may be regarded as a fundamental constant, though the proton would seem to be a less 'fundamental' particle than the electron.

The mass of the proton may conveniently be determined in atomic mass units, amu, one amu being defined as one sixteenth of the mass of the O^{16} atom, as discussed in section 2.3. Such determinations are made either mass spectroscopically [55] or by deriving small mass differences from the

Q-values of nuclear reactions [179]. For the atomic mass of the proton, M_a, both these methods yield a result with an uncertainty of 2 or 3 ppm, and the results obtained by the two different methods are essentially in agreement. To derive the proton mass in grams a knowledge of the conversion factor from amu to gm is required; this is just N amu $= 1$ gm, where N is Avogadro's number. The value of the proton mass in gm, M, is therefore subject to the same order of uncertainty as the value of Avogadro's number, i.e. about ± 25 ppm. In deriving the best values of the constants from measurements involving M it is therefore usual to substitute the quantity (M_a/N) for M and to treat M_a as 'exactly' known; Avogadro's number then appears in the analysis as a quantity whose best value is eventually to be determined.

CHAPTER V

THE DERIVATION OF THE BEST VALUES OF THE CONSTANTS

APART from the velocity of light, c, none of the constants can be measured directly with significant precision. Our present day knowledge of their magnitudes rests largely on the experiments described in the previous chapter, and on some from Chapter II, which are all measurements of quantities related in a known way to the constants. The problem is to find the 'best' (a term to be defined later) values of the constants from these measurements.

The analysis of the data has been very fully described in the literature [39] [40]; a very brief indication of the method will be given here. The first problem is the retention or rejection of the experimental data from which the constants are to be derived. This is done initially on the basis of the uncertainty of the quoted result: thus the early deflection methods of measuring e/m (section 2.5) have uncertainties of the order of 200 ppm, and so can be rejected as they have very low weight compared with recent determinations of, say, the proton magnetic moment (sections 4.2 and 4.3) with their uncertainties of only about 10 ppm. In some cases the experimental data is of high precision, but must be rejected because of the uncertainty of the theoretical expression in terms of the constants, e.g. the hyperfine structure of hydrogen, section 4.5.

The relations between the constants e, h, N, ..., K in number, and the n experimental data X_1^i, X_2^i, ..., X_n^i are of the form

$$e^{l_1}h^{m_1}N^{n_1} \ldots = X_1^i$$
$$e^{l_2}h^{m_2}N^{n_2} \ldots = X_2^i$$
$$\ldots \ldots \ldots \ldots \ldots \quad (5.1)$$

where l_1, $l_2 \ldots m_1$, $m_2 \ldots$ are the powers to which e, h, $N \ldots$ are raised. There are sufficient experimental data so that the number n exceeds the number of constants K whose best values are to be determined. No exact solutions of the equations (5.1) can of course be found, since the data X_1^i, $X_2^i, \ldots$ are subject to errors and the equations are not consistent, except by a very unlikely chance. Approximate values of $e, h, N, \ldots$ are known and it is possible to reduce (5.1) to linear form by writing

$$e = e_0(1+\delta_e)$$
$$h = h_0(1+\delta_h)$$
$$\ldots \ldots \ldots \ldots \quad (5.2)$$

where e_0, h_0, ... are the chosen 'origin values' of the constants and δ_e, δ_h, ... are all very small compared with unity. Equations (5.1) now become to a sufficiently good approximation

$$l_1\delta_e+m_1\delta_h+n_1\delta_N+ \ldots = X_1^i-(e_0^l h_0^{m_1}N_0^{n_1} \ldots) = Y_1$$
$$l_2\delta_e+m_2\delta_h+n_2\delta_N+ \ldots = X_2^i-(e_0^l h_0^{m_2}N_0^{n_2} \ldots) = Y_2$$
$$\ldots \ldots \ldots \ldots \ldots \ldots \ldots \ldots \ldots \ldots \ldots \ldots \ldots \ldots \quad (5.3)$$

This set of equations in the unknowns δ_e, δ_h, δ_N, ... is over-determined, i.e. $n > K$. The problem now is to find values δ_e^0, δ_h^0, δ_N^0, ..., which according to some criterion give the 'best' fit to the equations 5.3. This criterion is the condition of 'least squares'. If the values δ_e^0, δ_h^0, δ_N^0, ... are substituted back into the left-hand side of the equations 5.3 the result will yield, in general, not the quantity Y_1, Y_2, ..., but instead $Y_1(1+r_1)$, $Y_2(1+r_2)$, ..., where the residuals r_1, r_2, ... are all small compared with unity. The least squares condition governing the choice of δ_e^0, δ_h^0, δ_N^0, ... is then that the sum of the squares of the r's shall be a minimum. Before the analysis is applied attention must be paid to the measure of the uncertainty in the experimental quantities X_1^i, X_2^i, ..., that is to the 'weight' of each equation. Obviously a quantity X_n^i which has been measured with low precision must not be allowed to influence the final choice of the δ's as much as another, X_m^i, which has been measured with high precision. If the standard deviation in the determination of X_n^i was σ_n, and that of X_m^i was σ_m, then the appropriate weighting factors for the equations 5.3 containing X_n^i and X_m^i are $(1/\sigma_n^2)$ and $(1/\sigma_m^2)$ respectively.

The derivation of the least squares values of δ_e, δ_h, ... from equations 5.3 taking into account their appropriate weighting factors is a standard procedure [186]. Having found δ_e^0, δ_h^0, ... the 'output' values of the constants are

$$e^0 = e_0(1+\delta_e^0)$$
$$h^0 = h_0(1+\delta_h^0)$$
$$\dots \dots \dots \dots \tag{5.4}$$

These values can now be substituted back into equations 5.1 to obtain the output values X_1^0, X_2^0, ... which correspond to the observed or 'input' values X_1^i, X_2^i, ..., i.e.

$$(e^0)^{l_1}(h^0)^{m_1}(N^0)^{n_1} = X_1^0$$
$$(e^0)^{l_2}(h^0)^{m_2}(N^0)^{n_2} = X_2^0$$
$$\dots \dots \dots \dots \dots \dots \tag{5.5}$$

Any marked discrepancy between the experimental value X_n^i and the output value X_n^0, outside the limits defined by the standard deviation σ_n in the determination of X_n^i, points to a systematic error in X_n^i and gives grounds for the rejection of this particular result from the analysis.

A further important quantity which can be derived is the probable error or standard deviation of the output values e^0, h^0, N^0, ... The derivation is again a standard procedure, but since in some cases one or more of the quantities chosen for analysis may be not a fundamental constant but a quantity such as α, the fine structure constant $(2\pi e^2/hc)$, the estimation of the uncertainty of the individual constants must be made with some care [40].

As an example of the application of the above method an outline of the procedure adopted by Cohen, DuMond and their collaborators will be given.

The fundamental constants whose values are to be determined are e, m, h, N, and c; the data also involve the mass of the proton M (gm) ($= M_a$ (amu)$/N$) and, in the cases where X-ray measurements are involved, the conversion factor Λ from XU to cm. Of these it is possible to treat c and M_a as exactly known, since they have uncertainties of the order of 1 ppm, about one tenth of that of the best of the rest of the significant data. In addition, the Rydberg constant R_∞ known to 0·1 ppm, is given by

$$R_\infty = 2\pi^2 m e^4/h^3 c \qquad (5.6)$$

(section 2.7) and so is a means of eliminating one of the quantities m, e or h from the set; of these m was chosen to be eliminated, using the relation

$$m = \frac{R_\infty h^3 c}{2\pi^2 e^4} \qquad (5.7)$$

It was also decided to substitute for h the fine structure constant

$$\alpha = 2\pi e^2/hc \qquad (5.8)$$

since this quantity is directly determined by the deuterium fine structure experiment of Lamb (section 4.6). Thus

$$h = \frac{2\pi e^2}{\alpha c} \qquad (5.9)$$

In the final analysis, values of the four unknowns e, α, N, and Λ were derived from the experimental values of seven related quantities:

(1) *The short wavelength limit of the continuous X-ray spectrum* λ_0 (section 2.6d), which is related to the constants by

$$he^{-1}\Lambda^{-1} = V\lambda_0/c^2 \qquad (5.10)$$

in which V, the effective potential difference through which the electrons have fallen, is measured in emu, λ_0 is measured in XU, and e is in esu.

(2) *The magnetic moment of the proton in nuclear magnetons* (μ_p/μ_N) (section 4.2), which can be written as

$$\frac{\mu_p}{\mu_N} = \left(\frac{\mu_p}{\mu_e}\right)\left(\frac{\mu_e}{\mu_0}\right)\left(\frac{\mu_0}{\mu_N}\right). \tag{5.11}$$

Of the three bracketed ratios the first is known experimentally with very high precision and can be treated as exact (section 4.4). The second, the ratio of the 'anomalous' magnetic moment of the electron to the Bohr magneton is known theoretically:

$$\frac{\mu_e}{\mu_0} = 1 + \frac{\alpha}{2\pi} - 0\cdot328\,\frac{\alpha^2}{\pi^2} \tag{5.12}$$

plus higher order terms which are negligible. The coefficient of the last term as originally calculated [102] [157] was $-2\cdot973$, but this was later corrected to the value $-0\cdot328$ by Petermann [135] and Sommerfield [165]. The value $-2\cdot973$ was used by the 1955 reviewers [17] [43]: the change of 14 ppm in the value of (μ_e/μ_0) resulting from the use of the smaller coefficient makes changes ranging from 1 to 40 ppm in the values of the constants [18] [42] [57]. Because (μ_e/μ_0) differs from unity by only about 1 part in 1000, a very precise value for α is not needed in order to calculate the value of (5.12) to a precision sufficiently high for the value of (μ_e/μ_0) to be treated as exact.

The third ratio in (5.11), the ratio of the nuclear magneton to the Bohr magneton is, from their definitions, the ratio of the electron mass to the proton mass, $(m/M) = (Nm/M_a)$. Eliminating m by using (5.7) gives

$$\frac{\mu_p}{\mu_N} = \left(\frac{\mu_p}{\mu_e}\right)\left(\frac{\mu_e}{\mu_0}\right)\frac{2\pi^2 M_a e^4}{N R_\infty h^3 c} \tag{5.13}$$

or from (5.9)

$$\frac{\mu_p}{\mu_N} = \left(\frac{\mu_p}{\mu_e}\right)\left(\frac{\mu_e}{\mu_0}\right)\frac{\alpha^3 c^2 M_a}{N R_\infty 4\pi e^2} \tag{5.14}$$

i.e.

$$N e^2 \alpha^{-3} = \left(\frac{\mu_N}{\mu_p}\right)\left(\frac{\mu_p}{\mu_e}\right)\left(\frac{\mu_e}{\mu_0}\right)\frac{c^2 M_a}{4\pi R_\infty} \tag{5.15}$$

In this last expression, the quantities on the right-hand side are all known 'exactly' with the exception of the first. The experimental determination of (μ_p/μ_N) is the source of the uncertainty of the value of (5.15).

(3) *The gyromagnetic ratio of the proton*, which is defined in Chapter IV, may be written as

$$\gamma_p = \frac{4\pi\mu_p}{h} = \left(\frac{\mu_p}{\mu_e}\right)\left(\frac{\mu_e}{\mu_0}\right)\frac{\alpha^3 c}{4\pi e R_\infty}, \qquad (5.16)$$

using the same substitutions as in the discussion of the proton magnetic moment above, and the definition of the Bohr magneton $\mu_0 = he/(4\pi mc)$.

Equation 5.16 may be written

$$\alpha^3 e^{-1} = \gamma_p\left(\frac{\mu_e}{\mu_p}\right)\left(\frac{\mu_0}{\mu_e}\right)\frac{4\pi R_\infty}{c} \qquad (5.17)$$

where the quantities on the right-hand side are all precisely known with exception of γ_p (section 4.1).

(4) *The Faraday* (section 2.4), which may be written as

$$F = Ne/c, \qquad (5.18)$$

i.e.
$$Ne = cF, \qquad (5.19)$$

in which the experimentally determined quantity which has significant uncertainty is F.

(5) *The fine structure separation in deuterium*, $\Delta\nu_D$, which may be written as

$$\Delta\nu_D = \frac{\alpha^2 R_D c}{16}(1+K), \qquad (5.20)$$

where R_D is the Rydberg constant for deuterium and K is the small correction term involving α as given in equation 4.10. Rewriting (5.20) gives

$$\alpha^2 = \frac{16\Delta\nu_D}{R_D c(1+K)}, \qquad (5.21)$$

in which the uncertainty lies in the value of $\Delta\nu_D$.

(6) *The conversion factor from X-units to cm*, Λ (section 2.3), as determined from simultaneous measurements of X-ray wavelengths with a ruled grating and a calcite crystal. The

measured value Λ_m and the conversion factor may be equated:

$$\Lambda = \Lambda_m. \qquad (5.22)$$

(7) *The Avogadro number as determined by the X-ray method,* N (section 2.3), which involves a knowledge of the wavelength in XU of the X-rays used. In order to derive Avogadro's number the conversion factor Λ must be introduced:

$$N\Lambda^3 = N' . \qquad (5.23)$$

The seven equations 5.10, 5.15, 5.17, 5.19, 5.21, 5.22, and 5.23 are a set of the form of equations 5.1 (except that α has been used in place of h by using equation 5.9). The equations were linearized as described, given weights in inverse proportion to the squares of the standard deviations of the experimentally determined quantities, and a least squares fit was found for the variables δ_e^0, δ_α^0, ... of equation 5.4.

In a preliminary analysis Cohen, DuMond, and their collaborators found that the output values of the constants derived in this way showed marked inconsistencies with certain of the experimental data. The experiments which showed discrepancies were the early determination of (μ_p/μ_N) by Bloch and Jeffries, the Faraday as measured by using the silver cell and the short wavelength limit measurements of the continuous X-ray spectrum. Subsequent experiments have resolved the first of these discrepancies, but further work is needed before the other two can be judged with certainty. The reviewers rejected all the above determinations with the exception of the low voltage measurements of the X-ray limit, in which they had the most confidence. A table of the fundamental constants and related quantities is given in Appendix III.

Future revisions

No major survey has been made since 1955 and any future revision awaits significant results from new experiments. Small changes in the values of the constants have been occasioned by the corrected theoretical value of (μ_e/μ_0) but the revised values do not lie far outside the probable errors quoted in the 1955 revision [18] [42]. It seems that the procedure adopted in future revisions will be based on that of Cohen, DuMond, and others which has been outlined above, and that the experimental results chosen for inclusion in the analysis will be measurements of the same quantities as hitherto used, but with higher precision or reduced likelihood of systematic error. A danger not widely discussed in the literature and which may remain undetected by any analytical procedure has been pointed out by Bearden and Thomsen [18] in connexion with the velocity of light measurements of the 1930's: 'Assume that the experiments were not really independent, but that there was a subconscious psychological factor which tended to make each experimenter look for errors in his technique until he could check the then accepted value.* How do we know the psychological factor is not equally important today?'.

APPENDIX I

COMMONLY USED SYMBOLS

Except where it is stated otherwise, the units used in the text are those given below.

c Velocity of light; cm sec^{-1}.

e Magnitude of the charge on the electron; esu.

F The Faraday; emu (g equiv)$^{-1}$.

h Planck's constant; erg cm.

H Magnetic field intensity; emu (gauss).

k Boltzmann's constant; erg degC^{-1}.

m Mass of the electron; g.

M Mass of the proton; g.

M_a Mass of the proton; amu.

M_0 Mass of a (specified) nucleus; g.

N Avogadro's number; (g mole)$^{-1}$ (physical scale).

R_∞ Rydberg's constant for infinite nuclear mass; cm^{-1}.

R_H, R_D Rydberg's constant for hydrogen, deuterium; cm^{-1}.

* The author is grateful to Professor P. A. Franken for introducing him to the term "intellectual phase-locking" to describe this effect.

α The fine structure constant $= 2\pi e^2/(hc)$; dimensionless.

γ_p Gyromagnetic ratio of the proton; radian sec^{-1} gauss^{-1}.

λ Wavelength; cm.

Λ Conversion factor from X-units to cm; cm XU^{-1}.

μ_0 Bohr magneton $= he/(4\pi mc)$; erg gauss^{-1}.

μ_e Magnetic moment of the electron; erg gauss^{-1}.

μ_p Magnetic moment of the proton; erg gauss^{-1}.

μ_N Nuclear magneton $= he/(4\pi Mc)$; erg gauss^{-1}.

APPENDIX II

STANDARDS OF MEASUREMENT

THE result of any measurement involving dimensional quantities relies at some stage on a comparison with the internationally accepted standards. The importance of these standards in connexion with the experiments described here cannot be overlooked, especially as the results of some of the experiments approach the precision with which comparison can be made with the standards themselves.

1. Mass

The standard mass of the metric system is the International Prototype Kilogramme, a cylinder of 90 per cent platinum, 10 per cent iridium alloy preserved at the International Bureau of Weights and Measures at Sèvres, near Paris. Copies of this standard are in the possession of the countries signatory to the Metric Convention of 1875. These copies are compared from time to time with the International Prototype, and are available for standardization within the countries concerned. The comparisons may be made with a balance which, in the limit, can detect mass differences of about 10^{-6} gm, i.e. 1 part in 10^9, but the comparisons show that the relative stability of the standards is about 1 or 2 parts in 10^8. The limitation is probably one of surface films which build up on the standards during storage.

It should be noted that the standard is one of mass, but the experimentally determined quantity is often a force measured in terms of the gravitational force exerted on a standard mass. Such a situation has been described in the determination of the gyromagnetic ratio of the proton, section 4.1. In such a case the value of the acceleration due to gravity, g, at the site of the experiment must be known. The part played by g in the determination of the constants has been discussed by Huntoon and McNish [93] who conclude that although the most precise measurements of g, all by the pendulum method, appear to be consistent to 2 parts in 10^6, there may be a systematic error as large as 15 parts in 10^6. This may contribute to the uncertainty of all measurements which, directly or indirectly, involve g.

2. Length

The International Prototype Metre is a bar of 90 per cent platinum, 10 per cent iridium alloy of special winged X-form with an exposed neutral plane, kept at Sèvres. The metre is defined as the distance between two transverse lines in the neutral plane when the bar is at 0°C and supported in a specified manner. As in the case of the Prototype Kilogram, the Prototype Metre is available for comparison with the standards preserved by certain countries. The stability of these standards is about 1 part in 10^7 over periods of many years, and this represents also the order of magnitude of the precision of the intercomparison of standards, the limitation being the width of the marks on the bar and the smoothness and similarity of the edges of the marks.

Distances which are measured by surveying techniques, of importance in optical methods of measuring c, can be compared with the standard metre through the intermediary of a surveying tape, with a precision of between 1 part in 10^6 and 1 part in 10^7.

An improvement of the definition of the metre is likely to be made in terms of the wavelength of a suitable visible radiation in place of the material standard now in use. Wavelengths may be compared with a precision of between 1 part in 10^8 and 1 part in 10^9, and the re-definition of the metre awaits the choice of a suitable wavelength standard. This must be a source which gives a symmetrical narrow line reproducible to the above limits. It will undoubtably be a lamp containing a single isotope of zero nuclear spin, such as Kr^{84}, Hg^{198}, Cd^{114}, or Xe^{136}, and the metre will be defined in terms of the vacuum wavelength of a specified spectral line.

For some time (since 1907) the International Ångström has been defined by taking the wavelength in normal air (at 15°C and at a pressure of 1013250 dynes cm^{-2}, containing 0·03 per cent carbon dioxide and no water vapour) of the red cadmium line as 6438·4696 Ångströms, and in 1927 provisional international approval was given to the use of the relation 1 metre = 10^{10} International Ångströms, thus defining the metre in terms of a standard wavelength. All nine determinations of the metre in terms of the wavelength of the red cadmium line have agreed to ±3 parts in 10^7, but an improvement of at least one order of magnitude is likely by a different choice of wavelength standard.

3. Time

The mean solar second of Universal Time is defined as 1/86400 of the mean solar day. The length of the mean solar day is subject to variations due to the movement of the earth's pole and to seasonal variations in the rate of rotation of the earth. The magnitude of the corrections for these effects has been internationally agreed and can, with some uncertainty, be predicted. The resulting uncertainty in the value of the solar second is about 5 parts in 10^9. More serious is the fact that the value of the unit has varied by as much as 7 parts in 10^8 in the last hundred years, owing to a slow change in the rate of rotation of the earth.

For precise work the adopted standard is the second of Ephemeris Time, defined as the fraction 1/31556925·975 of the tropical year 1900. The difference between this and the solar second of Universal Time is now about 1·8 parts in 10^8; the value of this difference is published from time to time.

The unit of time is fundamentally established by astronomical observations extending over a period of years. The working standard of time interval is an oscillator producing an output at a frequency which can ultimately be compared with astronomical observations. Comparison of an unknown frequency with the standard can be made in a very short time. Until recently the most stable oscillators available were based on the resonance of a piezoelectric quartz crystal, commonly at 100 kc sec^{-1}, but frequency standards have now been developed using the transition between two energy states of a molecule (such as the inversion line of ammonia [83]) or the hyperfine levels of an atom (such as those of caesium [66]) both in the microwave region. Transitions of this sort can be used to define a frequency in terms of the properties of a particular molecule or atom and are therefore fundamental in character. It is likely that the unit of time interval will eventually be defined in terms of such a transition.

The measurements described in this book which involve time all involve, in practice, the measurement of frequency. Standards of frequency are maintained by several countries and standard frequency transmissions are regularly broadcast. These transmissions are normally of adequate precision, being known in frequency to at least 1 part in 10^8 at the transmitter. At large distances, where reflection of the waves from the ionosphere has occurred, there may be random changes of the received frequency, but these are only of significance in very precise work.

4. Electrical units

The only electrical quantity which need be mentioned here is that of current, the absolute ampere. This is defined as the current in two parallel straight conductors of infinite length and negligible cross-section which would produce 2×10^{-7} MKS unit of force between them per metre of length when placed one metre apart in a vacuum. The unit is established by measuring the force between two conductors in a current balance; since the electromagnetic force is compared with that due to gravity on a standard mass the value of the acceleration due to gravity g is involved in the measurement. The uncertainty of the determination of a current in terms of the absolute ampere is a few parts in 10^6, omitting the uncertainty in the value of g.

APPENDIX III

TABLE OF CONSTANTS

Cohen, DuMond, Layton, and Rollett, 1955 [43].

Velocity of light
$$c = 299793 \cdot 0 \pm 0 \cdot 3 \text{ km sec}^{-1}$$

Avogadro's number (physical scale)
$$N = (6 \cdot 02486 \pm 0 \cdot 00016) \times 10^{23} \text{ (g mole)}^{-1}$$

Planck's constant
$$h = (6 \cdot 62517 \pm 0 \cdot 00023) \times 10^{-27} \text{ erg sec}$$
$$\hbar = h/2\pi = (1 \cdot 05443 \pm 0 \cdot 00004) \times 10^{-27} \text{ erg sec}$$

Electronic charge
$$e = (4 \cdot 80286 \pm 0 \cdot 00009) \times 10^{-10} \text{ esu}$$
$$= (1 \cdot 60206 \pm 0 \cdot 00003) \times 10^{-20} \text{ emu}$$

Electron rest mass
$$m = (9 \cdot 1083 \pm 0 \cdot 0003) \times 10^{-28} \text{ g}$$

Proton rest mass
$$M = M_a/N = (1 \cdot 67239 \pm 0 \cdot 00004) \times 10^{-24} \text{ g}$$

Conversion factor from Siegbahn X units to cm
$$\Lambda = (1 \cdot 002039 \pm 0 \cdot 000014) \times 10^{-11} \text{ cm XU}^{-1}$$

Faraday constant (physical scale)
$$F = Ne = (2 \cdot 89366 \pm 0 \cdot 00003) \times 10^{14} \text{ esu (g equiv)}^{-1}$$
$$= (9652 \cdot 19 \pm 0 \cdot 11) \text{ emu (g equiv)}^{-1}$$

Charge-to-mass ratio of the electron
$$e/m = (5 \cdot 27305 \pm 0 \cdot 00007) \times 10^{17} \text{ esu gm}^{-1}$$
$$= (1 \cdot 75890 \pm 0 \cdot 00002) \times 10^{7} \text{ emu gm}^{-1}$$

Fine structure constant
$$\alpha = 2\pi e^2/(hc)$$
$$= (7 \cdot 29729 \pm 0 \cdot 00003) \times 10^{-3}$$
$$1/\alpha = 137 \cdot 0373 \pm 0 \cdot 0006$$

Atomic mass of proton (physical scale)
$$M_a = 1 \cdot 007593 \pm 0 \cdot 000003 \text{ amu}$$

Ratio proton mass to electron mass

$$M_a/(Nm) = 1836\cdot12 \pm 0\cdot02$$

Rydberg constant for infinite mass

$$R_\infty = 109737\cdot309 \pm 0\cdot012 \text{ cm}^{-1}$$

Rydberg constants for the light nuclei

$$R_H = 109677\cdot576 \pm 0\cdot012 \text{ cm}^{-1}$$
$$R_D = 109707\cdot419 \pm 0\cdot012 \text{ cm}^{-1}$$
$$R_{He^4} = 109722\cdot267 \pm 0\cdot012 \text{ cm}^{-1}$$

First Bohr radius

$$a_0 = h^2/(4\pi^2 m e^2) = \alpha/(4\pi R_\infty)$$
$$= (5\cdot29172 \pm 0\cdot00002) \times 10^{-9} \text{ cm}$$

Classical electron radius

$$r_0 = e^2/(mc^2) = \alpha^3/(4\pi R_\infty)$$
$$= (2\cdot81785 \pm 0\cdot00004) \times 10^{-13} \text{ cm}$$
$$r_0^2 = (7\cdot94030 \pm 0\cdot00021) \times 10^{-26} \text{ cm}^2$$

Gas constant per mole (physical scale)

$$R_0 = (8\cdot31696 \pm 0\cdot00034) \times 10^7 \text{ erg mole}^{-1} \text{ deg}^{-1}$$

Standard volume of a perfect gas (physical scale)

$$V_0 = 22420\cdot7 \pm 0\cdot6 \text{ cm}^3 \text{ atm mole}^{-1}$$

Boltzmann's constant

$$k = R_0/N = (1\cdot38044 \pm 0\cdot00007) \times 10^{-16} \text{ erg deg}^{-1}$$
$$= (8\cdot6167 \pm 0\cdot0004) \times 10^{-5} \text{ ev deg}^{-1}$$
$$1/k = 11605\cdot4 \pm 0\cdot5 \text{ deg ev}^{-1}$$

Stefan constant

$$\sigma = (\pi^2/60)(k^4/\hbar^3 c^2)$$
$$= (0\cdot56687 \pm 0\cdot00010) \times 10^{-4} \text{ erg cm}^{-2} \text{ deg}^{-4} \text{ sec}^{-1}$$

Second radiation constant

$$C_2 = ch/k = 1\cdot43880 \pm 0\cdot00007 \text{ cm deg.}$$

Bohr magneton

$$\mu_0 = he/(4\pi mc)$$
$$= (0\cdot92731 \pm 0\cdot00002) \times 10^{-20} \text{ erg gauss}^{-1}$$

Nuclear magneton

$$\mu_N = he/(4\pi Mc)$$
$$= (0\cdot505038 \pm 0\cdot000018) \times 10^{-23} \text{ erg gauss}^{-1}$$

Proton magnetic moment

$$\mu_p = 2\cdot79275 \pm 0\cdot00003 \text{ nuclear magnetons}$$
$$= (1\cdot41044 \pm 0\cdot00004) \times 10^{-23} \text{ erg gauss}^{-1}$$

Gyromagnetic ratio of the proton

$$\gamma_p = (2\cdot67530 \pm 0\cdot00004) \times 10^4 \text{ radians sec}^{-1} \text{ gauss}^{-1}$$

REFERENCES AND AUTHOR INDEX

1. ALVAREZ, L. W. and BLOCH, F., 1940, *Phys. Rev.* **57,**
111 42
2. ANDERSON, W. C., 1937, *Rev. Sci. Inst.* **8,** 239; 1941,
J. Opt. Soc. Am. **31,** 187 22
3. ANON., 1773, *Histoire de l'Academie Royale des
Sciences, Paris,* **1,** 213 20
4. ARAGO, D. F. J., 1838, *Comptes Rendus* **7,** 954; 1839,
Pogg. Ann. **46,** 28; 1850, *Comptes Rendus* **30,** 489 . 21
5. ASLAKSON, C. I., 1949, *Trans. Am. Geophys. Un.* **30,**
475 23
6. ASLAKSON, C. I., 1949, *Nature* **164,** 711 23
7. ASLAKSON, C. I., 1951, *Trans. Am. Geophys. Un.* **32,**
813 . . . . 23, 25
8. BABCOCK, H. D., 1923, *Astrophys. J.* **58,** 149; 1929,
ibid. **69,** 43 7
9. BÄCKLIN, E., 1935, *Z. Phys.* **93,** 450 4
10. BÄCKLIN, E. and FLEMBERG, H., 1936, *Nature* **137,**
655 3
11. BATES, S. J. and VINAL, G. W., 1914, *J. Am. Chem.
Soc.* **36,** 916 6
BATES, S. J. *See* 181
12. BEARDEN, J. A., 1931, *Phys. Rev.* **37,** 1210; 1935,
ibid. **48,** 385 4
13. BEARDEN, J. A., 1938, *Phys. Rev.* **54,** 698 . . . 5
14. BEARDEN, J. A., 1931, *Phys. Rev.* **38,** 2089 . . . 5
15. BEARDEN, J. A., JOHNSON, F. T., and WATTS, H. M.,
1951, *Phys. Rev.* **81,** 70 12
16. BEARDEN, J. A. and SCHWARZ, G., 1941, *Phys. Rev.*
59, 934 9
17. BEARDEN, J. A. and THOMSEN, J. S., 1955, "*A
Survey of Atomic Constants*", Johns Hopkins
University, Baltimore 17, 35, 37, 65

18. BEARDEN, J. A. and THOMSEN, J. S., 1959, *Am. J. Phys.* **27,** 569 . . . . 65, 67, 68

BENDER, P. L. *See* 52.

19. BERGSTRAND, E., 1952, *Recent Developments and Techniques in the Maintenance of Standards,* H.M.S.O. 21, 23

20. BERGSTRAND, E., 1956, *Handbuch der Physik* **24,** 1   23, 35

21. BERGSTRAND, E., 1949, *Nature* **163,** 338; 1949, *Ark. Mat. Astr. Fys.* **A36,** 1 . . . . . . 25, 32, 33

22. BERGSTRAND, E., 1950, *Nature* **165,** 405; 1950, *Ark. Fys.* **2,** 119; 1951, *ibid.* **3,** 479 33

23. BERGSTRAND, E., 1957, *Suppl. 1 al Nuovo Cimento* **6,** 224; 1957, *Ann. Franç. Chron.* **11,** 97. . . . 33, 35

24. BERINGER, R. and HEALD, M. A., 1954, *Phys. Rev.* **95,** 1474 55

25. BIRGE, R. T., 1945, *Am. J. Phys.* **13,** 63   . . 3, 4, 5

26. BIRGE, R. T., 1941, *Reps. Prog. Phys.* **8,** 90   . 22, 34

27. BIRGE, R. T., 1929, *Revs. Mod. Phys.* **1,** 1 . . . 18

BLAINE, L. R. *See* 136.

BLOCH, F. *See* 1.

28. BOL, K., 1950, *Phys. Rev.* **80,** 298 24

29. BÖMMEL, H. and DRANSFELD, K., 1958, *Phys. Rev. Letters* **1,** 234 35

30. BRADLEY, J., 1728, *Phil. Trans.* No. 406 . . . 20

31. BREIT, G. and RABI, I., 1931, *Phys. Rev.* **38,** 2082 . 54

32. BUCHERER, A. H., 1908, *Verh. der D. Phys. Ges.* **10,** 688; 1908, *Phys. Z.* **9,** 755; 1909, *Ann. Phys.* **28,** 513 6

33. BUSCH, H., 1922, *Phys. Z.* **23,** 438 6

34. CAMPBELL, J. S. and HOUSTON, W. V., 1932, *Phys. Rev.* **39,** 601 7

CHAFFEE, E. L. *See* 134.

35. CHU, D. Y., 1939, *Phys. Rev.* **55,** 175 13

36. CLASSEN, J., 1908, *Phys. Z.* **9,** 762; 1908, *Verh. der D. Phys. Ges.* **10,** 700 6

37. CLEWS, C. J. B. and ROBINSON, H. R., 1940, *Proc. Roy. Soc.* **A176,** 28 16

38. COHEN, E. R., 1952, *Phys. Rev.* **88**, 353 . . . 14, 15

39. COHEN, E. R., 1953, *Revs. Mod. Phys.* **25**, 709 . . 61

40. COHEN, E. R., CROWE, K. M., and DuMOND, J. W. M., 1957, *"The Fundamental Constants of Physics"*, Interscience Publishers, New York 12, 16, 61, 64

41. COHEN, E. R. and DuMOND, J. W. M., 1957, *Handbuch der Physik* **35**, 1 37

42. COHEN, E. R. and DuMOND, J. W. M., 1958, *Phys. Rev. Letters* **1**, 291 . . . . 65, 67

43. COHEN, E. R., DuMOND, J. W. M., LAYTON, T. W., and ROLLETT, J. S., 1955, *Revs. Mod. Phys.* **27**, 363 . . . . 3, 5, 14, 35, 37, 65, 73

44. COLLINGTON, D. J., DELLIS, A. N., SANDERS, J. H., and TURBERFIELD, K. C., 1955, *Phys. Rev.* **99**, 1622 46

45. COMPTON, A. H. and DOAN, R. L., 1926, *Proc. Nat. Acad. Sci. U.S.A.* **11**, 598 4
CONNOR, W. S. *See* 136.

46. CORNU, M. A., 1874, *Comptes Rendus* **79**, 1361; 1876, *Annales de l'Observatoire de Paris* **13**, 293. . . . 20

47. CRAIG, D. N. and HOFFMAN, J. I., 1953, *U.S. Nat. Bur. Stand. Circ.* **524**, 13; 1950, *Phys. Rev.* **80**, 487 6
CROWE, K. M. *See* 40.
DAYHOFF, E. S. *See* 174.

48. DAYHOFF, E. S., TRIEBWASSER, S. and LAMB, W. E., 1953, *Phys. Rev.* **89**, 106 . . . . 58, 59
DELLIS, A. N. *See* 44.
DICKE, R. H. *See* 191.

49. DIRAC, P. A. M., 1938, *Proc. Roy. Soc.* **A165**, 199 . 1
DOAN, R. L. *See* 45.

50. DORSEY, N. E., 1944, *Trans. Am. Phil. Soc.* **34**, Part 1, 1 23
DORSEY, N. E. *See* 149.
DRANSFELD, K. *See* 29.

51. DRINKWATER, J. W., RICHARDSON, O. and WILLIAMS, W. E., 1940, *Proc. Roy. Soc.* **A174**, 164 13

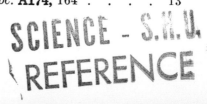

DRISCOLL, R. L. *See* 170.

52. DRISCOLL, R. L. and BENDER, P. L., 1958, *Phys. Rev. Letters* **1**, 413; 1958, *I.R.E. Trans.* **I-7**, 176.   39

53. DUANE, W., PALMER, H. H., and YEH, C. S., 1921, *J. Opt. Soc. Am.* **5**, 376 12

54. DuBRIDGE, L. A., 1933, *Phys. Rev.* **43**, 727 . . 8

55. DUCKWORTH, H. E., 1958, *"Mass Spectroscopy"*, Cambridge University Press 60

56. DuMOND, J. W. M., 1957, *Suppl. 1 al Nuovo Cimento* **6**, 68 37

57. DuMOND, J. W. M., 1958, *I.R.E. Trans.* **I-7**, 136   11, 65
DuMOND, J. W. M. *See* 40, 41, 42, 43 *and* 126.

58. DuMOND, J. W. M., LIND, D. A. and WATSON, B. B., 1949, *Phys. Rev.* **75**, 1226 16

59. DUNNINGTON, F. G., 1933, *Phys. Rev.* **43**, 404; 1937, *ibid.* **52**, 475 . . . . 6, 10

60. DUNNINGTON, F. G., 1939, *Revs. Mod. Phys.* **11**, 70   10

61. DUNNINGTON, F. G., HEMENWAY, C. L. and ROUGH, J. D., 1954, *Phys. Rev.* **94**, 592 10

62. EDDINGTON, A., 1946, *"Fundamental Theory"*, Cambridge University Press 1

63. EDDINGTON, A., 1939, *"The Philosophy of Physical Science"*, Cambridge University Press 1

64. ESSEN, L., 1950, *Nature*, **165**, 582; 1950, *Proc. Roy. Soc.* **A204**, 260 24

65. ESSEN, L. and GORDON-SMITH, A. C., 1948, *Proc. Roy. Soc.* **A194**, 348 23

66. ESSEN, L. and PARRY, J. V. L., 1958, *Phil. Trans.* **250**, 45 72

67. FIELD, J. C. and SERIES, G. W., 1959, *Proc. Symposium on Interferometry at the N.P.L.*, H.M.S.O. . 14

68. FIZEAU, H. L., 1849, *Comptes Rendus* **29**, 90; 1850, *Pogg. Ann.* **79**, 167 20
FLEMBERG, H. *See* 10.

69. FLORMAN, E. F., 1955, *J. Res. Nat. Bur. Stand.* **54**, 335 25
FORBES, G. *See* 193.

70. Foucault, J. L., 1850, *Comptes Rendus* **30**, 551; 1850, *Pogg. Ann.* **81**, 434 21

71. Foucault, J. L., 1862, *Comptes Rendus* **55**, 501, 792; 1863, *Pogg. Ann.* **118**, 485 21

72. Franck, J. and Hertz, G., 1914, *Verh. der D. Phys. Ges.* **16**, 10 9

73. Franken, P. A. and Liebes, S., 1956, *Phys. Rev.* **104**, 1197; 1959, *ibid.* **116**, 633 50

74. Froome, K. D., 1952, *Proc. Roy. Soc.* **A213**, 123 . 25

75. Froome, K. D., 1954, *Proc. Roy. Soc.* **A223**, 195 25, 28

76. Froome, K. D., 1958, *Proc. Roy. Soc.* **A247**, 109 25, 35

77. Froome, K. D., 1958, *Nature* **181**, 258 . . . 28, 35

Fukushima, I. *See* 97.

78. Galileo Galilei, 1638, *Discorsi e dimostrazione matematiche*, Elzevir edition, 43 20

79. Gardner, J. H., 1951, *Phys. Rev.* **83**, 996 . . . 48

80. Gardner, J. H. and Purcell, E. M., 1949, *Phys. Rev.* **76**, 1262 48

81. Gheury de Bray, M. E. J., 1927, *Astr. Nach.* **230**, 449; 1931, *Nature* **127**, 522; 1934, *ibid.* **133**, 464, 948 20

82. Gilliam, O. R., Johnson, C. M., and Gordy, W., 1950, *Phys. Rev.* **78**, 140 34

83. Gordon, J. P., Zeiger, H. J., and Townes, C. H., 1955, *Phys. Rev.* **99**, 1264 72

Gordon-Smith, A. C. *See* 65.

Gordy, W. *See* 82.

Guenther, A. H. *See* 141.

84. Gutton, C., 1912, *J. de Phys.* **2**, 196 22

85. Hahn, E. L., 1950, *Phys. Rev.* **77**, 297 41

86. Hammer, W., 1914, *Ann. Phys.* **43**, 653 6

87. Hardy, W. A., 1959, *Bull. Am. Phys. Soc.* **4**, 37 . 51

88. Hart, C. A., 1948, *Bull. Géod. No.* **10**, 307 . . . 23

Hemenway, C. L. *See* 61.

Hertz, G. *See* 72.

Hipple, J. A. *See* 164 *and* 170.

Hoffman, J. I. *See* 47.

89. HOPPER, V. D. and LABY, T. H., 1941, *Proc. Roy. Soc.* **A178**, 243   3

90. HOUSTON, W. V., 1937, *Phys. Rev.* **52**, 75 . . .   3

91. HOUSTON, W. V., 1927, *Phys. Rev.* **30**, 608 . . .   13

    HOUSTON, W. V. *See* 34 *and* 104.

92. HOUSTOUN, R. A., 1938, *Nature* **142**, 833; 1941, *Proc. Roy. Soc. Edinburgh* **A61**, 102; 1950, *ibid.* **A63**, 95   21

    HOYT, H. C. *See* 126.

93. HUNTOON, R. D. and McNISH, A. G., 1957, *Suppl. 1 al Nuovo Cimento* **6**, 146   70

94. HUTCHISON, C. A. and JOHNSTON, H. L., 1940, *J. Am. Chem. Soc.* **62**, 3165   5

95. HUTCHISON, D. A., 1944, *Phys. Rev.* **66**, 144 . .   5

    HUTCHISON, D. A. *See* 100.

96. HÜTTEL, A., 1940, *Ann. Phys.* **37**, 365 . . .   22, 32

    IEVENS, A. *See* 168.

97. ISHIDA, Y., FUKUSHIMA, I., and SUETSUGU, T., 1937, *Sci. Papers Inst. Phys. Chem. Res. Tokyo* **32**, 57 .   3

98. JANNEY, D. H., 1957, *Phys. Rev.* **105**, 1138. . .   36

99. JEFFRIES, C. D., 1951, *Phys. Rev.* **81**, 1040 . . .   45

    JOHNSON, C. M. *See* 82.

    JOHNSON, F. T. *See* 15.

    JOHNSTON, H. L. *See* 94.

100. JOHNSTON, H. L. and HUTCHISON, D. A., 1942, *Phys. Rev.* **62**, 32   5

    KARLSONS, K. *See* 168.

101. KAROLUS, A. and MITTELSTAEDT, O., 1928, *Phys. Z.* **29**, 698   22

102. KARPLUS, R. and KROLL, N. M., 1951, *Phys. Rev.* **81**, 73 . . . .   52, 65

103. KAUFMAN, W., 1897, *Ann. Phys.* **61**, 544; *ibid.* **62**, 596; 1898, *ibid.* **65**, 431   6

104. KINSLER, L. E. and HOUSTON, W. V., 1934, *Phys. Rev.* **45**, 104, 134; 1935, *ibid.* **46**, 533   7

105. KIRCHNER, F., 1929, *Phys. Z.* **30**, 773; 1931, *Ann. Phys.* **8**, 975; 1932, *ibid.* **12**, 503   6

106. KIRCHNER, F., 1924, *Phys. Z.* **25,** 302   6
107. KIRCHNER, F. and WILHELMY, W., 1957, *Suppl. 1 al Nuovo Cimento* **6,** 246   39
    KIRKPATRICK, P. *See* 151.
    KLEIN, D. J. *See* 126.
108. KOENIG, S. H., PRODELL, A. G., and KUSCH, P., 1952, *Phys. Rev.* **88,** 191   55
109. KRETSCHMAR, G. G., 1933, *Phys. Rev.* **43,** 417 . .   16
    KROLL, N. M. *See* 102.
110. KUSCH, P., 1955, *Phys. Rev.* **100,** 1188   56
    KUSCH, P. *See* 108 *and* 138.
    LABY, T. H. *See* 89.
111. LAMB, W. E., 1952, *Phys. Rev.* **85,** 259   59
    LAMB, W. E. *See* 48 *and* 174.
112. LAMB, W. E. and RETHERFORD, R. C., 1947, *Phys. Rev.* **72,** 241; 1950, *ibid.* **79,** 549; 1951, *ibid.* **81,** 222   58
113. LAWRENCE, E. O., 1926, *Phys. Rev.* **28,** 947 . .   10
    LIEBES, S. *See* 73.
    LIND, D. A. *See* 58.
114. LUKIRSKY, P. and PRILEZEAV, S., 1928, *Z. Phys.* **49,** 236   9
    MCDONALD, D. F. *See* 127.
115. MACKENZIE, I. C. C., 1954, *Ordnance Survey Professional Papers No. 19,* H.M.S.O.   33
116. MCKINLEY, D. W. R., 1950, *J. Roy. Astr. Soc. Canada* **44,** 89   21
    MCNISH, A. G. *See* 93.
    MASSEY, H. S. W. *See* 125.
117. MERCIER, J., 1924, *J. Phys. et le Radium* **5,** 168 .   24
118. MERRILL, P. W., 1917, *Astrophys. J.* **46,** 357 . .   14
119. MICHELSON, A. A., 1879, *Nature* **21,** 94, 120; 1885, *Nautical Almanac, Washington,* 235; 1924, *Astrophys. J.* **60,** 256; 1927, *ibid.* **65,** 1   21
120. MICHELSON, A. A., PEASE, F. G., and PEARSON, F., 1935, *Astrophys. J.* **82,** 26   21

121. MILLIKAN, R. A., 1908, *Phys. Rev.* **26,** 198; 1910, *Phil. Mag.* **19,** 209; 1913, *Phys. Rev.* **2,** 136; 1917, *Phil. Mag.* **34,** 1; 1947, *"Electrons (+ and −), Protons, Photons. Neutrons and Cosmic Rays"*, University of Chicago Press   3

122. MILLIKAN, R. A., 1916, *Phys. Rev.* **7,** 355 . . .   9

123. MILNE, A. E., 1935, *"Relativity, Gravitation and World Structure"*, Oxford University Press . . .   1

124. MITTELSTAEDT, O., 1929, *Ann. Phys.* **2,** 289 . .   22
MITTELSTAEDT, O. See 101.

125. MOTT, N. F. and MASSEY, H. S. W., 1949, *"The Theory of Atomic Collisions"*, Oxford University Press   54

126. MULLER, D. E., HOYT, H. C., KLEIN, D. J., and DUMOND, J. W. M., 1951, *Phys. Rev.* **81,** 468 . .   16

127. MULLIGAN, J. F. and MCDONALD, D. F., 1957, *Am. J. Phys.* **25,** 180   35
MURTY, J. S. See 144.

128. NEWCOMB, S., 1885, *Nautical Almanac, Washington,* 112   21

129. NILSSON, A., 1953, *Ark. Phys.* **6,** 513   9

130. OHLIN, P., 1940, *Ark. Math. Astron. Phys.* **B27,** No. 10; 1942, *ibid.* **A29,** No. 3; *ibid.* **B29,** No. 4; 1944, *ibid.* **A31,** No. 9; 1946, *ibid.* **A33,** No. 23 . .   12

131. OLPIN, A. R., 1930, *Phys. Rev.* **36,** 251   9

132. PACKARD, M., and VARIAN, R., 1954, *Phys. Rev.* **93,** 941   41
PALMER, H. H. See 53.
PARRY, J. V. L. See 66.
PEARSON, F. See 120.
PEASE, F. G. See 120.

133. PERROTIN, H., 1900, *Comptes Rendus* **131,** 731; 1902, *ibid.* **135,** 881; 1908, *Annales de l'Observatoire de Nice,* 11   20

134. PERRY, C. T. and CHAFFEE, E. L., 1930, *Phys. Rev.* **36,** 904   6

135. PETERMANN, A., 1957, *Helv. Phys. Acta* **30,** 407 .   52, 65

136. PLYLER, E. K., BLAINE, L. R. and CONNOR, W. S.,
     1955, *J. Opt. Soc. Am.* **45,** 102 34
137. POOLE, K. M., 1953, *Proc. Phys. Soc.* **B66,** 542 . . 6
     PRILEZEAV, S. *See* 114.
138. PRODELL, A. G. and KUSCH, P., 1950, *Phys. Rev.*
     79, 1009; 1952, *ibid.* **88,** 184 56
     PRODELL, A. G. *See* 108.
     PURCELL, E. M. *See* 80.
     RABI, I. *See* 31.
139. RAMSEY, N. F., 1956, *"Molecular Beams",* Oxford
     University Press 54
140. RANK, D. H., 1954, *J. Opt. Soc. Am.* **44,** 341 . . 34
141. RANK, D. H., GUENTHER, A. H., SHEARER, J. N., and
     WIGGINS, T. A., 1957, *J. Opt. Soc. Am.* **47,** 148 . . 34
142. RANK, D. H., RUTH, R. P. and VAN DER SLUIS,
     K. L., 1952, *Phys. Rev.* **86,** 799 34
143. RANK, D. H., SHEARER, J. N. and WIGGINS, T. A.,
     1954, *Phys. Rev.* **94,** 575 34
144. RAO, B. R. and MURTY, J. S., 1956, *Nature* **178,** 160   35
     RETHERFORD, R. C. *See* 112.
     RICHARDSON, O. *See* 51.
145. ROBINSON, C. F., 1939, *Phys. Rev.* **55,** 423 . . . 15
     ROBINSON, G. *See* 186.
146. ROBINSON, H. R., 1936, *Phil. Mag.* **22,** 1129 . . . 16
     ROBINSON, H. R. *See* 37.
147. ROEHR, W. W., 1933, *Phys. Rev.* **44,** 866 . . . 8
148. RÖMER, O., 1676, *J. des Sçavans* **4,** 276 20
149. ROSA, E. B. and DORSEY, N. E., 1907, *Bull. Bur.*
     Stand. **3,** 433 33
150. ROSA, E. B. and VINAL, G. W., 1916–17, *Bull. Bur.*
     Stand. **13,** 479 6
151. ROSS, P. A. and KIRKPATRICK, P., 1934, *Phys. Rev.*
     45, 223; *ibid.* **46,** 668 15
     ROUGH, J. D. *See* 61.
     RUTH, R. P. *See* 142.
152. RYDBERG, J. R., 1888–89, *Kongl. Sv. Vetensk. Akad.*
     Handl. **23/2,** No. 11; 1890, *Phil. Mag.* **29,** 331 . . 13

153. RYMER, T. B. and WRIGHT, K. H. R., 1952, *Proc. Roy. Soc.* **A215,** 550 15
154. SANDERS, J. H., 1959, *Nature* **183,** 312 36
155. SANDERS, J. H., 1957, *Suppl. 1 al Nuovo Cimento* **6,** 242 46
     SANDERS, J. H. *See* 44.
156. SCHÖLDSTRÖM, K. O. R., 1955, *"The Determination of Light Velocity in Öland, 1955",* Aga Company, Stockholm 33
     SCHWARZ, G. *See* 16.
157. SCHWINGER, J., 1948, *Phys. Rev.* **73,** 416 . . 52, 65
158. SCOTT, A. F., 1953, *U.S. Nat. Bur. Stand. Circ.* **524,** 1   6
159. SERIES, G. W., 1957, *"The Spectrum of Atomic Hydrogen",* Oxford University Press 14
     SERIES, G. W. *See* 67.
160. SHANE, C. D. and SPEDDING, F. H., 1935, *Phys. Rev.* **47,** 33 15
161. SHAW, A. E., 1934, *Phys. Rev.* **44,** 1006; 1937, *ibid.* **51,** 58; 1938, *ibid.* **54,** 193. 6
     SHEARER, J. N. *See* 141 *and* 143.
162. SIEGBAHN, M., 1931, *"Spektroskopie der Röntgenstrahlen",* 2nd. Ed., Springer, Berlin; 1943, *Nature,* **151,** 502 4
163. SÖDERMAN, M., 1935, *Nature* **135,** 67 4
164. SOMMER, H., THOMAS, H. A., and HIPPLE, J. A., 1951, *Phys. Rev.* **82,** 697 42
165. SOMMERFIELD, C. M., 1957, *Phys. Rev.* **107,** 328   52, 65
     SPEDDING, F. H. *See* 160.
166. STEWART, R. L., 1934, *Phys. Rev.* **45,** 488 . . . 6
167. STILLE, U., 1943, *Z. Phys.* **121,** 133 23
168. STRAUMANIS, M., IEVENS, A., and KARLSONS, K., 1939, *Z. Phys. Chem.* **B42,** 143 5
     SUETSUGU, T. *See* 97.
169. THIBAUD, J., 1927, *J. Phys. et le Radium* **8,** 13 . 4
     THOMAS, H. A. *See* 164.

170. THOMAS, H. A., DRISCOLL, R. L. and HIPPLE, J. A.,
     1950, *J. Res. Nat. Bur. Stand.* **44,** 569; 1950, *Phys.
     Rev.* **78,** 787   38
     THOMSEN, J. S. *See 17 and* 18.
171. THOMSON, J. J., 1898, *Phil. Mag.* **46,** 528; 1903, *ibid.*
     5, 354   2
172. THOMSON, J. J., 1897, *Phil. Mag.* **44,** 293 . . .   6
     TOWNES, C. H. *See* 83.
173. TOWNSEND, J. S., 1897, *Proc. Camb. Phil. Soc.* **9,** 244   2
     TRIEBWASSER, S. *See* 48.
174. TRIEBWASSER, S., DAYHOFF, E., S. and LAMB, W. E.,
     1953, *Phys. Rev.* **89,** 98 . . . . 58, 59
175. TRIGGER, K. R., 1956, *Bull. Am. Phys. Soc.* **1,** 220   46
176. TU, Y., 1932, *Phys. Rev.* **40,** 662   5
     TURBERFIELD, K. C. *See* 44.
177. TYRÉN, F., 1938, *Z. Phys.* **109,** 722   4
178. VAN ATTA, L. C., 1931, *Phys. Rev.* **38,** 876; 1932,
     ibid. **39,** 1012   10
     VAN DER SLUIS, K. L. *See* 142.
179. VAN PATTER, D. M. and WHALING, W., 1954, *Revs.
     Mod. Phys.* **26,** 402   61
     VARIAN, R. *See* 132.
     VINAL, G. W. *See* 11 *and* 150.
180. WALLER, C. K., 1956, *Cartography* **1,** No. 3 . . .   33
181. WASHBURN, E. W. and BATES, S. J., 1912, *J. Am.
     Chem. Soc.* **34,** 1341   6
     WATSON, B. B. *See* 58.
     WATTS, H. M. *See* 15.
182. WEICHERT, E., 1899, *Ann. Phys.* **69,** 739 . . .   6
183. WEYL, H., 1922, *"Space, Time, Matter"*, Methuen,
     London   1
     WHALING, W. *See* 179.
184. WHEATSTONE, C., 1834, *Phil. Trans.* 583 . . .   21
185. WHIDDINGTON, R., and WOODROOFE, E. G., 1935,
     Phil. Mag. **20,** 1109   10
186. WHITTAKER, E. and ROBINSON, G., 1944, *"The Cal-
     culus of Observations"*, Blackie, London   63

187. WICHERS, E., 1954, *J. Am. Chem. Soc.* **76,** 2033 .   6
     WIGGINS, T. A. *See* 141.
188. WILHELMY, W., 1957, *Ann. Phys.* **19,** 329 . . . 39
     WILHELMY, W. *See* 107.
189. WILLIAMS, R. C., 1938, *Phys. Rev.* **54,** 558 . . . 15
     WILLIAMS, W. E. *See* 51.
190. WILSON, H. A., 1903, *Phil. Mag.* **5,** 429 . . . 2
191. WITTKE, J. P. and DICKE, R. H., 1954, *Phys. Rev.*
     96, 530 56
192. WOLF, F., 1927, *Ann. Phys.* **83,** 849 6
     WOODROOFE, E. G. *See* 185.
     WRIGHT, K. H. R. *See* 153.
193. YOUNG, J. and FORBES, G., 1881, *Proc. Roy. Soc.* **32,**
     247; 1882, *Phil. Trans.* **173,** Part 1 20
     ZEIGER, H. J. *See* 83.

INDEX